PUTNAM'S
NATURE FIELD BOOKS

Companion books to this one

Mathews	American Wild Flowers
	American Trees and Shrubs
	Wild Birds and Their Music
Durand	Wild Flowers in Homes and Gardens
	My Wild Flower Garden
	Common Ferns
Lutz	Insects
Loomis	Rocks and Minerals
Eliot	Birds of the Pacific Coast
Armstrong	Western Wild Flowers
Alexander	Birds of the Ocean
Anthony	North American Mammals
Thomas	Common Mushrooms
Sturgis	Birds of the Panama Canal Zone
Miner	Seashore Life
Breder	Marine Fishes of the Atlantic Coast
Morgan	Ponds and Streams
Longyear	Rocky Mountain Trees and Shrubs
Olcott Putnam	Field Book of the Skies
Beebe Tee-Van	The Shore Fishes of Bermuda
Schrenkeisen	Fresh-Water Fishes of North America North of Mexico

FIELD BOOK OF
COMMON ROCKS AND MINERALS

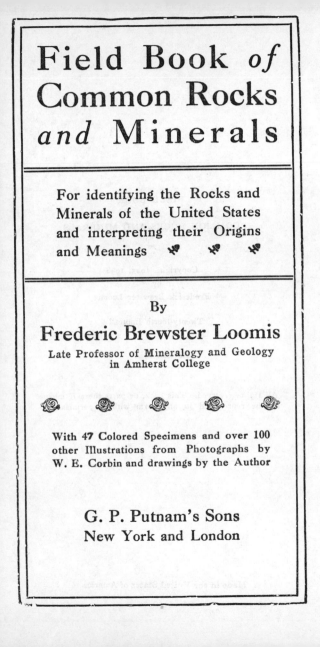

Field Book *of* Common Rocks *and* Minerals

For identifying the Rocks and Minerals of the United States and interpreting their Origins and Meanings

By

Frederic Brewster Loomis

Late Professor of Mineralogy and Geology in Amherst College

With 47 Colored Specimens and over 100 other Illustrations from Photographs by W. E. Corbin and drawings by the Author

G. P. Putnam's Sons
New York and London

FIELD BOOK
OF
COMMON ROCKS AND MINERALS

Copyright, 1923, 1948
by
Frederick Brewster Loomis

Twenty-fourth Impression

Revised 1948

DEDICATED

TO

MY MOTHER

WHO ENCOURAGED ME WHILE A BOY TO GATHER

MINERALS, ROCKS AND FOSSILS.

PREFACE

Everyone, who is alert as he wanders about this world, wants to know what he is seeing and what it is all about. Here and there with the aid of capable guides a few have been introduced into the sphere of that wide and fascinating knowledge of Nature which has been so rapidly accumulated during this and the latter part of the last century. It is a full treasure house constantly being enriched, but unfortunately the few who have been initiated have soon acquired a technical language and habit, so that their knowledge and new acquisitions are communicated to but few. The public at large, not having the language nor an interpreter at hand, has come almost at once to a barrier which few have the time or patience to surmount.

Latterly it has become clear that the largest progress cannot be made if the knowledge of any branch of Science is confined to ⌐ few only. The most rapid advances have been made where many men are interested and enthusiastic. In no science should there be a difficult barrier between the amateur and the professional student. All Nature is equally open for everyone to study, and there should never be created obstacles as by the use of terminology not easily acquired by anyone. Of late these barriers have been in part broken down and competent students have written guides which anyone can follow, and soon begin to know the plants, trees, birds, insects, etc. So far no one has attempted to make the study of minerals and rocks so direct and simple that everyone can get a start. Most books on minerals, and practically all those on rocks are written for school courses, and to say the least chill any enthusiasm which is naturally aroused by the finding of interesting looking rocks or minerals.

The purpose of this book is first of all to provide a means of identifying minerals and rocks by such methods as are practical without elaborate equipment or previous training: and second to suggest the conditions under which the various minerals and rocks were formed, so that, at the first contact, one may get a conception of the events which have anteceded the mineral or rock which has been found. For this purpose keys have been worked out for determining the rocks and minerals by such obvious features as color, hardness, etc. Each mineral or rock is introduced by a summary of its characters, then the features by which it may be distinguished from any other similar mineral are given, after which its mode of origin and its meanings are considered. For those interested in the composition of the minerals, it is given in chemical symbols with each mineral. Most classifications of minerals are based on the composition, all the sulphides, carbonates, etc., being grouped together, but in this book, because the popular interest and commercial uses are primarily in the metal present, the minerals are grouped in each case about the chief metal, all the minerals of iron being grouped together, for instance.

A few minerals and rocks which are not strictly common have been included such as gems and meteorites; the gems because they are of intense interest to their owners and are often simply perfect examples of a fairly common mineral; and such forms as meteorites because it is important that, if one should run across one, it should be recognized, and so not lost to the world.

The book is freely illustrated, those minerals in which color is important for identification being illustrated in colors, and those which are black, or in which the color is not a determining factor, are shown in either photographic or outline figures.

In the introductory chapter there are explanations of the terms used in describing minerals, and of the systems in which they are grouped. A knowledge of the systems may not be a necessity, but it is a great help in determining minerals, and is very important in understanding why the individual minerals take the varied forms which are characteristic of them. These systems will be better understood after a few minerals have been gathered and examined.

It is hoped the book will help those who have already some knowledge of rocks and minerals, and especially that it will tempt many to begin an acquaintance with the rocks and minerals which are all about them, and are the foundation on which our material progress is built. Rocks and minerals have some advantages over most objects which are collected in that they neither require special preparation before they can be kept, nor do they deteriorate with time.

The author will appreciate corrections or suggestions as to better presentation of the material in this book.

F. B. L.

Amherst, Mass.

CONTENTS

LIST OF PLATES

(AT END OF BOOK)

xiii

LIST OF PLATES

LIST OF PLATES

LIST OF PLATES

LIST OF PLATES

LIST OF PLATES

FIELD BOOK OF
COMMON ROCKS AND MINERALS

CHAPTER I

AN INTRODUCTION

Why Why should one be interested in rocks and minerals? Because the whole world is made of rocks and minerals. They are the foundations on which we build. From them we draw all our metals, and the extent to which we utilize our minerals is a measure of the advance of our civilization. Fragments of rock are the soil from which, by way of the plants, we draw our food, and ultimately our life. The rocks make wild or gentle scenery, one at least of the sources of pleasure. Knowledge of rocks and minerals is then knowledge of fundamentals, of ultimate sources. Between finding the raw materials and their present uses there are usually many steps (so many that we forget that the beginning and end are united), as for instance in your watch. It is made of gold. brass, steel, agate, glass, and perhaps has luminous radium paint on the hands. It is a long way from finding and mining gold, chalcopyrite, hematite, carnotite, etc., through the raw materials, gold, copper, iron, etc., to the finished watch, but the minerals are the foundations of the watch; and it took centuries to find them and learn one by one how to use them, from the gold

10,000 years ago down to the radium within the last fifty years. Then too there is joy in going out into Nature's wild and raw places, joy in being on the foundations of the earth, joy in the scenery, in the beauty of the minerals themselves.

But why collect the rocks and minerals? First because this is the way to know them. Both mineral and rocks require careful examination in order to see all those fine points by which they are distinguished. It is often necessary to compare one with another to get in mind the differences of form, color, streak, though with increasing familiarity these characteristics are recognized at first sight. It is the repeated examination which makes a rock tell the story of the country from which it came. Our first attempts to read the story give us only the most general facts. Nature's book, written in the rocks, has to be read closely, often between the lines. Until we are used to the characters in which the words are written, we read slowly. When they look at Nature's book, always open, most people do not read; for they do not know their letters. Every mineral is a letter, every rock a word, and we learn to read as we learn the minerals and rocks, and every time we go over them we get more facts coming out. The place where a rock or mineral occurs is of course the relation between them, and is involved in reading the story. No one today is a perfect reader. We are all learning to see more in the rocks day by day. So it is important to have the rocks and minerals where they can be handled and repeatedly examined, where we can turn to them in our leisure moments. Don't stop when you have learned the name of a mineral or rock. You need more. See what it means. Secondly, minerals have beauties of form, color, and structure, and they do not fade. They will be as perfect in ten years as when found. We are all naturally crows, and love to gather the objects which interest us. It is not a bad habit, and only needs directing. Cultivate it. Have a hobby, and minerals and rocks are a good one; for they are like treasures in Heaven which "neither moth nor rust doth corrupt." Not only will they give you pleasure, but they will be a constructive education, training the eye to see, and the mind to think straight. No one ever regretted the time and effort spent in collecting either minerals or rocks.

Collecting In order to make a collection valuable two or three rules must be observed. In the case of rocks, collect large enough samples so that they will be characteristic, and clear in their make-up. The standard size for rocks is 3 x 4 inches on top and one to two inches thick according to the nature of the rock. Tiny fragments do not give the character of the rock as well, and they are all the time getting into confusion. **Every specimen should be labeled,** with at least its name and the exact locality from which it came. Composition, structural features, associations, and classification may be added, the more the better; for each item adds to the information and interest of the specimen. One may make his own labels or have printed blanks, and may put as much care and art into the labels as desired, the more the better. One thing is very important and that is to have a number on the label with a corresponding one on the specimen, so that in case they should get separated, they may be readily brought together, even by one who is not familiar with the individual specimens. Lastly, give your collection as good a place as possible, either in drawers, boxes or in a case. The specimens are worth being kept in order and where they can be readily seen and compared. Nature is systematic, and there is a reason for the order in which rocks and minerals are taken up. It is desirable either that this order, or some one of the orders of Nature appear in the collection. In this book the metals are the basis of classification, all those minerals primarily related to one of the metals being grouped together.

In collecting minerals, the size of the specimens can not be so regularly followed, but it should be followed when collecting non-crystalline minerals, and when possible. Crystals however are chosen from a variety of points of view, as perfection of form, color, examples of cleavage, twinning, etc.; so that in many cases smaller or larger examples must appear in the collection. It is always desirable that as many variations of a rock or mineral as possible should appear in the collection, and in many cases examples of the matrix from which the crystals came. When crystals are tiny, it is well to place them in vials, that they may not be lost.

AN INTRODUCTION

Where Where shall we start in making a collection? Near home. Get the local minerals and rocks first, and then range as widely as possible. The best places are bare and exposed rocks, especially where fresh and unweathered surfaces are available. Quarries and where there has been blasting along roads offer fine opportunities. Fissures and cavities in the rocks are especially likely to have fine crystals, and in all localities continued search will reveal a surprising number of different minerals. The greatest variety occur in metamorphic rocks, or where igneous rocks come in contact with other rocks, but even the sedimentary rocks have a goodly range of minerals. All through the glaciated regions of the northern United States lie scattered boulders brought from afar, which will yield a surprising number of minerals and variety of rocks.

Equipment One may start with a very simple equipment, a geologist's or stone mason's hammer which can be obtained at any hardware store, being sufficient for field work. Rocks should be broken, so as to show fresh surfaces and to get below the disintegrating effects of weathering. At home one should have a streak plate (a piece of unglazed porcelain), a set of hardness minerals (see page 20), and a small bottle each of hydrochloric and nitric acid. A pocket lens is useful in order to see more clearly the form of small minerals. These things can be purchased of any Naturalist's Supply Co., like Ward's Natural Science Establishment, P.O. 24,

Beachwood Sta., Rochester, N. Y., or the Kny-Scheerer Corp., 483 First Ave., New York City. Success depends upon a quick eye, and persistent hunting. When traveling, opportunities are offered at frequent intervals to see and get new specimens.

Study Your Collection   Be sure and see the meaning in each rock and mineral. The history of the country is revealed in its rocks and minerals. Note whether the rocks are horizontal or folded, whether they change character from place to place, or vertically. In going over a piece of country you may locate an ancient mountain system now leveled, by noting a series of metamorphic rocks, with a central core of granite, the roots of former mountains. Don't be afraid to draw conclusions from what you see. Later, when the opportunity offers, look up the region in the geological folio, bulletin, or map of that section, and check up your findings. These geological folios and bulletins, of which there is one for nearly every region, are a great help to collectors in suggesting where to look for various rocks and minerals. Write to the Director of the U. S. Geological Survey, Washington, D. C., for a catalogue of the publications of the United States Survey, or find out from him what are the maps or folios for the region in which you are interested. These U. S. publications cost but little. When opportunity presents itself, visit other collections. In them you will see some of the minerals or rocks which have puzzled you, and there is nothing quite so satisfactory as seeing the rocks or minerals themselves. No description can always be so convincing. Then too you will get suggestions as to localities that you can visit.

Literature   As your collection grows, if you find you have special interest in one or another branch of the field, you can get books giving more details in that line; and at the back of this book will be found a list of such books.

CHAPTER II

ON THE FORMS AND PROPERTIES OF MINERALS

Rocks
All we know of the earth by direct
observation is confined to less than
four miles depth; though by projecting downward
the layers of rock that come to the surface, we
may fairly assume a knowledge of the structure
down to six or eight miles depth. This outer
portion is often referred to as the "crust of the
earth," but the idea that the deeper portions are
molten is no longer held. This outer portion is
made of rocks, and a rock may be defined as, *a
mass of material, loose or solid, which makes up an
integral part of the earth*, as granite, limestone, or
sand. The rocks (except glassy igneous ones)
are aggregates of one or more minerals; either in
their original form like the quartz, feldspar and
mica of granite, or in a secondary grouping,
resulting from the units having been dislodged
from their primary position and regrouped a
second time, as in sandstone or clay.

Minerals
Since the rocks are aggregates of
minerals, it is best to take up the
minerals first. A mineral may be defined as *a
natural inorganic substance of definite chemical
composition*. It is usually solid, generally has

crystalline structure, and may or may not be bounded by crystal faces. *A crystal is a mineral, bounded by symmetrically grouped faces, which have definite relationships to a set of imaginary lines called axes.* There are between 1100 and 1200 minerals, of which 30 are so frequently present, and so dominant in making up the rocks, that they are termed *rock-forming minerals.* About 150 more occur frequently enough so that they can be termed common minerals, and one may expect to find a fairly large proportion of them. Some of these are abundant in one part of the country and rare in others, but this book is written to cover the United States, and so all those which have a fair abundance are included, though some will only be found in the west and others mostly in the east. Then there are some more minerals which are really rare, but which are cherished because of their beauty of color, and are used as gems. These are mentioned, and many of the gems are simply clear and beautiful examples of minerals, which in dark or cloudy forms are much more common. If one finds any of these rare minerals which are not mentioned in this book, he must turn to one of the larger mineralogies mentioned in the literature list to determine them.

Crystal Structure A crystal is a mass of molecules, all of the same composition. A molecule in its turn is made up of atoms, and each atom is a unit mass of an element. Thus the calcite molecule is made up of one unit or atom of calcium, one of carbon, and three of oxygen ($CaCO_3$). These atoms are held together by an attraction, and make a molecule. and for the study of minerals the molecule is the unit. The mineral, calcite, is a mass of molecules all like the one above, and each molecule so small as to be invisible even with the aid of the most powerful microscope. When calcite is in crystal form, the molecules, like ranks of soldiers, are arranged each in its place, each at a definite distance from the other. While each molecule may vibrate or wiggle within certain limits it does not leave its place. (The comparison with soldiers is a good one for the molecules of one layer, but it must be remembered that in a crystal there are also like spacings and ranks up and down as well.) As long as the molecules remain in fixed ranks, up and down, forward and back, and sideways, the crystal is perfect. Calcite may be heated until it melts and becomes liquid. Then the molecules leave their definite arrangement and move about in all sorts of directions, like the soldiers after ranks have broken. So long as the molecules are thus free to move about but keep together, the substance is a liquid. There are cases when the molecules in this disorder take fixed positions without falling into ranks. Such minerals are non-crystalline and usually appear glassy. If still greater heat is applied to the mineral in liquid form, a point is reached (the vapor point), above which the molecules go flying away from each (like soldiers in a panic), each seeking to get as far from the other as possible, so only a container will prevent their dissipation. When in this condition a mineral is gaseous. When cooled, the reverse order obtains. The molecules of gas gather into a miscellaneous mob or liquid: and if this is further cooled (but not too suddenly), they fall into ranks and make a crystal. This may be illustrated with water. When above 212° F. it is steam (molecules wildly dissipated); when between 212° and 32° it is water (molecules close to each other, but milling like a herd of cattle); and when below 32° it is ice, the molecules ranged in perfect order, rank on rank.

Crystal Systems With all the possible forms that crystals can and do take, there are six systems of arrangement. First there is the case where ranks, files, and vertical rows are all equal, and now to be scientific, instead of talking about ranks, files, etc., we use the term axes to express these ideas: the files or arrangements from front to back, being called the *a axis*, the ranks, or side to side arrangement the *b axis*, and the vertical arrangement the *c axis*. (See Plate 1.) These axes are imaginary lines, but they represent real forces.

Isometric system When the axes are all equal and at right angles to each other, a crystal is said to be in the **isometric system.** The cube is the basal form and each side is known as a face. The ends of the axes come to the middle of the cube faces. The essential feature of this system is that whatever happens to one axis must happen to all, which is another way of saying that all the axes are equal. If we think of the cube as having the corners cut off, we would have a new face on each of the eight corners, in addition to the six cube faces. Then if each of these new faces were enlarged until they met and obliterated the cube faces, an eight-sided figure, the octahedron, would result. In this the axes would run to the corners. Another modification of the cube would be to bevel each of its twelve edges, making twelve new faces in addition to the six cube faces. If we think of these new faces being developed until they meet and obliterate the cube faces, there will result a twelve-sided figure, the dodecahedron. And the 24 edges of the dodecahedron could be beveled to make a 24-sided figure, and so on. Of course in Nature the corners are not cut, nor the edges beveled, but as a result of the interaction of the forces expressed by the axes and the distribution of the molecules, the molecules arrange themselves in a cube, octahedron, dodecahedron or combination of these basal forms.

Crystal formation   Crystals are formed in liquids as they cool or evaporate and can no longer hold the minerals in solution. Crystals start about a center or nucleus, and molecule by molecule. the orderly arrangement is increased and the crystal grows, there being no size which is characteristic. If free in the liquid the crystal grows perfectly on all sides, but if crystals are growing side by side, there comes a time when they interfere with each other. Then the free faces continue to grow and the orderly internal arrangement is maintained, though externally there is interference.

Tetragonal system In the second or **tetragonal system** one axis (the c axis) is different from the other two, but all three are still at right angles with each other. This is saying scientifically that the lines of force are greater or less in one direction than in the other two, but they act at right angles to each other. The a and the b axes are equal and anything that happens to one of these two must happen to the other, but need not happen to the c axis. Thinking of the molecules that arrange themselves under this system of forces, it is clear that the simplest form will be a square prism, *i.e.*, front to back, and from side to side the numbers of molecules will be equal, but up and down there will be a greater or lesser number. If the eight corners of this prism were cut, and these corner faces increased in size until they met, the resulting octahedron would be longer (or shorter) from top to bottom than from side to side or front to back, but the measurement from front to back would be equal to the one from side to side. In this system we may have the vertical edges of the prism beveled, and not have to bevel the horizontal ones, or we may bevel the horizontal edges and not the vertical ones. There is no dodecahedron in this system or in any other system than the isometric. The forms in this tetrahedral system are really a combination of the four sides of the square prism with such modifications as equally affect them all, with two ends which may be flat, or pyramidal, or modified pyramidal faces.

The third system has all three axes
Orthorhombic system unequal, but all three are still at right angles with each other. This is saying that the lines of force in the crystals are all at right angles to each other but of unequal value. The faces in this case are all in pairs. What happens at one end of an axis must happen at the opposite end, but does not need to happen at the ends of any of the other axes. We are dealing with pairs of faces (one at either end of an axis), and if three such pairs are combined in the simplest manner, the resulting figure will be a rectangular prism. If we cut the eight corners of this prism and enlarge the faces until they meet, the result is an octahedron, in which the distance from top to bottom, from side to side, or from front to back is not the same in any two cases. (See Plate 2.) In this system if a face is made by beveling one edge of the prism there must be a corresponding face on the edge diagonally opposite, but there does not have to be one on any of the other edges. However if a corner is cut, that face affects all the axes and so all the corners must be cut. A great many crystals occur in this system, and some of them which are prismatic in shape may give trouble, for it is not uncommon for the vertical edges of the prism to be so beveled, that two of the original prism faces are obliterated, and the two remaining faces added to the four new faces make a six-sided prism, which at first glance seems to belong to the

hexagonal system. (See Plate 3, fig. 3.) Close examination however will show that, instead of all the prism faces being alike, as would be necessary for the hexagonal system, they are really in pairs, and one pair at least will be distinguished in some way, such as being striated, pitted, or duller.

Monoclinic system The fourth system has all the axes unequal, the a axis and the b axis at right angles to each other, but the c axis is inclined to the a axis, meeting it at some other than a right angle. The **monoclinic system** is like the orthorhombic system except that it leans, or is askew, in one direction. The result is that the faces at the ends of the b axis are rhombohedral, while the others are rectangular. As in the foregoing system, the faces are in pairs at opposite ends of the axes; and as in the orthorhombic system, a face may occur on one edge and only have to be repeated on the edge diagonally opposite. The simplest form in this system will be made by combining the three pairs of faces at the opposite ends of the axes, which gives a prism, which is rectangular in cross section, but leans backward (or forward) if placed on end. As in all the systems, if a corner is cut, all must be cut; and if these corner faces are extended to meet each other, an octahedron results, in which, as in the prism, no two axes are equal. If this octahedron is properly orientated (*i.e.* with the a and b axes horizontal), it will lean forward or backward. Many minerals belong to this system; and, as in the orthorhombic system, it is not uncommon to have the vertical edges so beveled that two of the prism faces are obliterated, and the remaining two prism faces with the four new faces make a six-sided prism, which seems hexagonal. (See plate 3, figure 3.) However, such a pseudo-hexagonal prism may be recognized by at least one pair of the faces having distinguishing marks (striæ, pits, or dullness), instead of all being just alike.

Triclinic
system
The fifth or **triclinic system** has all the axes unequal, and no two of them intersect at right angles. As in the two preceding systems the faces occur in pairs at the opposite ends of the axes. This is the most difficult system in which to orientate a crystal, but fortunately only a few crystals occur in this system, such as the feldspars.

Hexagonal
system
Lastly there is a group of crystals which have four axes, one vertical, and three in the horizontal plane which intersect each other at angles of 60°, all these three being equal to each other, but different from the vertical axis. The simplest form in this system is the six-sided prism. If one corner of this prism is cut all must be, and if these corner faces are extended to meet each other, a double-six-sided pyramid results. In this system if one of the vertical edges of the prism is beveled, all must be, but the horizontal edges need not be; or the horizontal edges may be beveled and the vertical ones not. The ends as they are related to the c axis may be

developed independently of the prism, and so the prism may be simply truncated by a flat end, or have pyramids on either end.

Hemihedral forms   In this system it is quite common to have forms which result from the development of each alternate face of either the prism or the double pyramid. In the case of the prism, if every alternate face is developed (and the others omitted) a three-sided prism results, as in tourmaline. In the case of the double pyramid if the three alternate faces above are united with the three alternate faces below, a six-sided figure is formed, which is known as the rhombohedron, as all the faces are rhombohedral in out-line and all equal. These forms in which only half the faces are developed are known as **hemihedral forms.** The same sort of thing may happen in the isometric system in the case of the octahedron, and also in the case of the octahedron of other systems. When half the faces of the octahedron are developed, two above unite with two below and make a four-sided figure, known as a tetrahedron. (See plate 10.) While tetrahedrons may occur in any of the first five systems they are not common outside the isometric system.

Twinning   Another modification of the simple forms which will be met occasionally is **twinning.** By this is meant two crystals growing together as though placed side by side on some one of the faces, and then revolved until the two axes which would normally be parallel are at some definite angle with each other, 60°, or

180° which is commoner. The surface of contact between the two crystals is called the *composition face*, and as no more material can be added on that face the crystals continue to grow developing the other faces, and we find faces in contact with each other which should be at the opposite end or other side of the crystals. This contact of faces which should not come in contact, and the presence of reentrant angles are indications of twinning. In some minerals the twinning may be repeated time and again, and if the twinning is on one of the end faces a branching structure results, as in frost and snow crystals, or the multiple twinning may be of crystals growing side by side when the final form will approximate a series of thin sheets placed side by side as in some feldspars. The peculiar forms characteristic of individual minerals are taken up under the respective minerals.

Other important properties of minerals are hardness, cleavage, specific gravity, streak, luster, and color.

Hardness

Hardness may be defined as the mineral's resistance to abrasion or scratching. It is measured by comparing a mineral with Moh's scale, a set of ten minerals arranged in the order of increasing hardness, as follows:

1	talc	6	feldspar
2	gypsum	7	quartz
3	calcite	8	topaz
4	fluorite	9	corundum
5	apatite	10	diamond

A set for measuring hardness may be purchased from any dealer in mineral supplies. For rough determination, as in the field, the following objects have the hardness indicated; the finger nail $2\frac{1}{4}$, a penny 3, a knife blade about 5.5, and glass not over 6. In testing, a mineral is harder than the one it will scratch, and softer than the one by which it is scratched. For instance, if a mineral will scratch calcite and is scratched by fluorite, it is between 3 and 4 in hardness, say 3.5. When two samples mutually scratch each other they are of equal hardness. Care must be used in determining hardness, especially with the harder minerals; for often, when testing a mineral, the softer one will leave a streak of powder on the harder one, which is not a scratch. One should always rub the mark to make sure it is really a groove made by scratching.

Cleavage   **Cleavage** is the tendency, characteristic of most minerals, and due to the arrangement of their molecules, to cleave or break along definite planes. The cleavage of any mineral is not irregular or indefinite, but characteristic for each mineral, and always parallel to possible or actual faces on the crystal, and always so described. For instance galena has three cleavages, all equally good, and parallel to the cube faces; so it is said to have cubic cleavage. In the same way fluorite has octahedral cleavage, and calcite rhombic cleavage. In some minerals cleavage is well developed in one plane, and less developed in other planes, or it may be lacking altogether. The varying degrees of perfection by which a mineral cleaves are expressed as, perfect or imperfect, distinct or indistinct, good or poor, etc.

Specific gravity   The **specific gravity** of a mineral is its weight compared with the weight of an equal volume of water, and is therefore the expression of how many times as heavy as water the mineral is. For instance the specific gravity of pyrite is 5.1, which is saying it is 5.1 times as heavy as water. In a pure mineral the specific gravity is constant, and an important factor in making final determinations. As ordinarily obtained, a piece of pure mineral is weighed in air, which value may be called x. It is then immersed in water and again weighed, and this value is called y. The difference between the weight in air and that in water is the weight of an equal volume of water. Then we have the following formula: specific gravity $= \dfrac{x}{x - y}$.

Various balances have been devised for making these measurements, but any balance which will weigh small objects accurately, may be adapted to specific gravity work, by hanging a small pan under the regular weighing pan. When using this balance, care is taken to see that the lower pan is always submerged in water, even while the mineral is being weighed in air, so that when weighed in water in the lower pan, the weight of this lower pan has already been considered.

Streak   By **streak** is meant the color of the mineral when powdered. For some minerals, especially metallic ores, it is of great importance, for it remains constant, though the color of the surface of the mineral changes materially. It is most readily determined by rubbing a corner of the mineral on a piece of unglazed porcelain. Small plates, known as "streak plates" are made for this purpose.

Luster   The **luster** of a mineral is the appearance of its surface by reflected light, and it is an important aid in determining many minerals. Two types of luster are recognized; metallic, the luster of metals, most sulphides and some oxides, all of which are opaque on their thin edges; and non-metallic, the luster of minerals which are more or less transparent on their thin edges, and most of which are light colored. The common non-metallic lusters are; vitreous, the luster of glass; resinous, the appearance of resin; greasy, oily appearance; pearly, the appearance of mother-of-pearl; silky, like silk due to the fibrous structure; adamantine, brilliant like a diamond; and dull, as is chalk.

Color   When used with caution **color** is of the utmost importance in determining minerals, especially in making rapid determinations. In metallic minerals it is constant and dependable; but in the non-metallic minerals it may vary, due to the presence of small amounts of impurities which act as pigments.   Color depends on chemical composition, and when not influenced by impurities is termed *natural;* but when the color is due to some inclosed impurity it is termed *exotic.*   In this latter case caution must be used in making determinations.   Many minerals are primarily colorless, but take on exotic colors as a result of the presence of small quantities of impurities; for instance, pure corundum is colorless, but with a trace of iron oxide present becomes red, and is called the ruby, or with a trace of cobalt becomes blue and is called sapphire.

CHAPTER III

THE MINERALS

KEY TO THE MINERALS, BASED ON HARDNESS, COLOR, ETC.

OPAQUE COLORS

Color	Hard-ness	Streak	Remarks	Mineral
Red				
scarlet	2.5	scarlet	surface tarnishes black	prousite
	2.5	vermilion	surface scarlet to dark red	cinnabar
ochre	7	white	noncrystalline	jasper
	6	ochre red	color red to almost black	hematite
rose	4	white	effervesces in warm acid	rhodochrosite
dark	4	orange		zincite
	2.5	purplish red	surface tarnishes black	pyrargyrite
brownish	3.5	brownish red		cuprite
Orange	3.5	white to yellowish		pyromorphite
	1–1½	orange		realgar
Blue	5.5–6	white	in igneous rocks	sodalite
azure	4	azure		azurite
sky	7&4.5	white	blade-like crystals	cyanite
turquoise	6	blue	noncrystalline	turquoise
	2–4	white		chrysocolla
Green				
malachite	3.5	lighter green		malachite
olive	6.5–7	white	in igneous rocks	olivine
	3.5	white to yellow		pyromorphite
	2	white	mica-like cleavage	chlorite
	1	white	greasy feel, color light to dark olive green	talc
yellowish	6.5	white		epidote
	2.5–4	white	color yellow green to olive	serpentine
Yellow				
golden	2.5	shining	noncrystalline	gold
brassy	6	greenish-black	usually crystalline	pyrite
	6	greenish-gray	color pale brassy yellow, usually non-crystalline	marcasite
	5.5	greenish-black	colors nitric acid green	millerite
	4	greenish-black	color golden similar to gold	chalcopyrite
	3.5	dark brown	purplish tarnish on surface	tetrahedrite
bronze	5.5	pale brownish-black	color with coppery cast	niccolite
	4	dark gray-black	with speedy black tarnish	pyrrhotite
	3	gray-black	brownish with bluish tarnish	bornite
	2.5	shining	coppery red color	copper
sulphur	3.5	white to yellowish	compact masses	pyromorphite
	2	yellow		sulphur
	1–3		earthy masses	carnotite

25

OPAQUE COLORS—*Continued*

Color	Hard-ness	Streak	Remarks	Mineral
Brown				
violet	1½	shining	tarnishes black	cerargyrite
yellowish	7.5	white	4-sided prisms	zircon
	6.5	gray		cassiterite
	5.5	ochre yellow	compact to earthy masses	limonite
	5	brownish-yellow		goethite
	4.5	black		wolframite
	3.5	yellowish-brown		sphalerite
	3.5	white		siderite
grayish	7.5	white	often twinned	staurolite
	6.5	pale brown		rutile
	3.5	white to yellowish	earthy masses	pyromorphite
reddish	7	white	dodecahedrons & trapezohedrons	garnet
Black	6.5	gray		cassiterite
	6	reddish-brown		franklinite
	6	black	magnetic	magnetite
	5.5	dark brown		chromite
	5.5	black	yellow precipitate in sulphuric acid	wolframite
	5–6	black	non-magnetic	ilmenite
	5–6	brownish-black	compact masses	psilomelane
	5	brownish-yellow	surface often brownish	goethite
	3.5	dark brown	tetrahedrons	tetrahedrite
	2.5	silvery	fresh surfaces silver color	silver
	2.5	scarlet	fresh surfaces bright red	prousite
	2.5	purplish red	fresh surfaces red	pyrargyrite
	2	black	earthy masses	pyrolusite
	1	steel gray	greasy feel	graphite
Metallic				
Gray		black	tarnishes black, bluish, or green	chalcocite
....	2.5	lead gray	sectile	argentite
	2.5	lead gray	cubic cleavage	galena
	2	lead gray	long prismatic crystals	stibnite
	1.5	bluish gray	in scales	molybdenite
steel	5.5	gray black	rose color in nitric acid	smaltite
	4.5	steel gray	very heavy	platinum
	4	reddish black	often in striated prisms	manganite
	1	gray	with greasy feel	graphite
silvery	5.5	black		arsenopyrite
	2.5	silvery	tarnishes black on exposure	silver
reddish	5.5	gray black	rose color in nitric acid	cobaltite
pearly	1–1½	shining	exposed surfaces violet brown	cerargyrite
White, with impurities	4	white	porcelainous masses, effervesces in acid	magnesite
grayish or	2	white	earthy masses, greasy feel	kaolin
yellowish	1–3	white	earthy masses	bauxite
	1	white	greasy feel, fibrous or scaly	talc

THE MINERALS

FIELD BOOK OF AMERICAN MINERALS

TRANSPARENT OR TRANSLUCENT COLORS

Color	Hardness	Remarks	Mineral
Colorless or with faint tinges of color due to impurities	10	in octahedrons	diamond
	9	in hexagonal prisms	corundum
	8	in hexagonal prisms	topaz
	7	in three-sided prisms	tourmaline
	7	in hexagonal prisms	quartz
	7	non-crystalline	chalcedony
	7 or 4.5	cubes with beveled edges	boracite
	6	non-crystalline, pearly luster	opal
	5.5	rhombohedrons	willemite
	5.5	trapezohedrons	analcite
	5.5	tufts of needle-like crystals	natrolite
	5.5	sheaf-like bundles of crystals	stilbite
	5	hexagonal prisms with basal cleavage	apatite
	5	effervesces in acid	smithsonite
	5	becomes jelly-like in acid	calamine
	4.5	monoclinic prisms	colemanite
	4	in cubes	fluorite
	3.5	effervesces in acid, but one cleavage	aragonite
	3.5	effervesces in acid, heavy	cerrusite
	3	effervesces in acid, rhomboidal cleavage	calcite
	3	no effervescence, but soluble in nitric acid	anglesite
	2.5	in cubes tastes of salt	halite
	2	soluble in water, sweetish taste	borax
	2	1 perfect cleavage, and two imperfect cleaves at 66 with each other	gypsum
White or with faint tinges of color due to impurities, such as pink, bluish, etc.	7	hexagonal prisms	quartz
	7	non-crystalline	chalcedony
	7 or 4.5	cubes with beveled edges	boracite
	6	non-crystalline, pearly luster	opal
	6	cleavage in 3 directions, good in 2 and imperfect in the other	feldspar
	5.5	short eight-sided prisms	pyroxene
	5.5	long six-sided prisms	amphibole
	5.5	trapezohedrons	analcite
	5.5	tufts of needle-like crystals	natrolite
	5.5	sheaf-like bundles of crystals	stilbite
	5.5	rhombohedrons	willemite
	5	effervesces in acid	smithsonite
	5	becomes jelly-like in acid	calamine
	4.5&7	cubes with beveled edges	boracite
	4.5	monoclinic prisms	colemanite
	4	effervesces in acid, porcelainous	magnesite
	3.5-4	effervesces in acid, heavy, red color in flame	strontianite
	3.5	effervesces in acid, heavy, green color in flame	witherite
	3.5	effervesces in warm acid, rhomboidal cleavage	dolomite
	3.5	effervesces in acid, cleavage in one direction only	aragonite
	3.5	effervesces in acid, heavy, does not color flame	cerrusite
	3-3.5	no effervescence, cleavage in three directions at right angles	anhydrite

TRANSPARENT OR TRANSLUCENT COLORS—*Continued*

COLOR	HARD-NESS	REMARKS	MINERAL
	3	effervesces in acid, rhomboidal cleavage	calcite
	3	tabular crystals, heavy, green color in flame	barite
	2–3	cleaves in thin elastic sheets	mica
	2.5	cleaves in cubes	cryolite
	2.5	cubes, soluble in water, salty taste	halite
	2	1 perfect cleavage, and 2 less perfect ones	gypsum
	2	cleaves in thin non-elastic sheets	chlorite
	2	soluble in water, tastes sweet	borax
	1	greasy feel	talc
Green	9	hexagonal prisms	oriental emerald
	8	octahedrons	spinel
	7.5	hexagonal prisms	beryl
	7	three-sided prisms	tourmaline
	7	dodecahedrons or trapezohedrons	garnet
	7	non-crystalline	phrase or plasma
	6.5–7	non-crystalline, olive color	olivine
	6.5	yellow green color, rather opaque	epidote
	6	non-crystalline, pearly luster	opal
	5.5	short eight-sided prisms	pyroxene
	5.5	long six-sided prisms	amphibole
	5	hexagonal prisms	apatite
	4	cubes	fluorite
	3.5	effervesces in acid	cerrusite
	2.5–4	somewhat greasy feel, massive or fibrous	serpentine
	2	in mica-like scales, non-elastic	chlorite
	1	greasy feel, fibrous or scaly	talc
Red	9	hexagonal prisms	ruby
	8	octahedrons	spinel
	7	three-sided prisms	tourmaline
	7	dodecahedrons or trapezohedrons	garnet
	7	hexagonal	rose quartz
	7	non-crystalline	jasper or carnelian
	6	pearly luster	fire opal
	4	cubes, rose tints	fluorite
	2–3	pink mica-like scales	lepidolite
Blue	9	hexagonal prisms	sapphire
	7 & 4.5	blade-like crystals	cyanite
	6	non-crystalline masses	turquoise
	5.5–6	in igneous rocks	sodalite
	4	azure color	azurite
	3.5	effervesces in acid, heavy	cerrusite
	2–4	earthy masses, turquoise color	chrysocolla
Violet	7	hexagonal prisms	amethyst
	4	cubes	fluorite
Yellow	9	hexagonal prisms	oriental topaz
	8	octahedrons	spinel
	8	hexagonal prisms	topaz
	4	cubes	fluorite

COLOR	HARD-NESS	REMARKS	MINERAL
Brown	9	hexagonal prisms	corundum
	8	octahedrons	spinel
	7.5	four-sided prisms	zircon
	7	hexagonal prisms	smoky quartz
	7	three-sided prisms	tourmaline
	7	non-crystalline	flint
	6	non-crystalline	opal
	5.5	short eight-sided prisms	pyroxene
	5.5	long six-sided prisms	amphibole
	2–3	cleaves into thin sheets	mica
Black	9	hexagonal prisms	corundum
	8	octahedrons	spinel
	7	three-sided prisms	tourmaline
	5.5	short eight-sided prisms	pyroxene
	5.5	long six-sided prisms	amphibole
	2–3	cleaves in thin sheets	mica

THE GOLD GROUP

Gold was undoubtedly the first metal to be used by primitive man; for, occurring as it did in the stream beds, its bright color quickly attracted the eye, and it was so soft, that it was easily worked into various shapes, which, because they did not tarnish, became permanent ornaments. The metal is associated with the very earliest civilizations, being found in such ancient tombs as those at Kertsch in Crimea and in northern Africa and Asia Minor. It was used in the cloisonné work of Egypt 3000 years B.C. In America the Indians, especially to the south, were using it long before the continent was discovered.

Of all the metals gold is the most malleable, and its ductility is remarkable, for a piece of a grain's weight (less than the size of a pin head) can be drawn out into a wire 500 feet long; and it can be beaten into a thin leaf as thin as $\frac{1}{250000}$ of an inch in thickness, and thus a bit, weighing only a grain, can thus be spread over 56 square inches.

It forms very few compounds, but has a considerable tendency to make alloys (*i.e.*, mixtures with other metals without the resulting compound losing its metallic character). In Nature gold is never entirely pure, but is an alloy, usually with silver, there being from a fraction of 1% up to 30% of the silver with the gold, the more silver, in the alloy the paler the color of the gold. Australian gold is the purest, having but about .3% of silver in it, while Californian gold has around 10% and Hungarian gold runs as high as 30% of silver. Another alloy fairly abundant in Nature is that with tellurium, such as *calaverite* ($AuTe_2$) which is a pale brassy yellow, similar to pyrite, but with the hardness of but 2.5. Another combination includes gold, silver and tellurium, *sylvanite*, ($AuAgTe_4$) a silvery white mineral with a hardness of but 2. Such combinations are known as tellurides and the calvarite is mined as a source of gold at Cripple Creek, Colo., while the sylvanite is one of the important ores of gold in South Africa. Occasionally gold is also found alloyed with platinum, copper, iron, etc. Jewelers make several alloys, "red gold" being 3 parts gold and 1 of copper, "green gold" being the same proportions of gold and silver, and "blue gold" being the combination of gold and iron. Our gold coins are alloys, nine parts gold and one of copper, to give them greater durability. Most of the gold recovered from nature is found native, *i.e.*, the pure metal, or with some alloy.

**Gold
Au, Pl. 5**
Usually non-crystalline, but occasionally showing cube or octahedral faces of the isometric system; hardness 2.5; specific gravity 19.3; color golden yellow; luster metallic; opaque.

Gold is mostly found as the metal and is readily recognized by its color, considerable weight, hardness, malleability, and the fact that it does not tarnsh. It usually occurs in quartz veins in fine to thick threads, scales or grains, and occasionally in larger masses termed "nuggets." It is insoluble in most liquids so that when weathered from its original sites, it was often washed down into stream beds, to be found later in the sands or gravels, or even in the sea beaches. When thus found it is termed "placer gold," and its recovery is placer mining. Most of the original discoveries of gold have been in these placer deposits; and from them it has been traced back to the ledges, from which it originally weathered. In the placer deposits the size of the particles varies from fine "dust" up to large nuggets, the largest found in California weighing 161 pounds; but the largest one found in the world was the "Welcome Nugget," found in Australia, and weighing 248 pounds. When gold was discovered in California in 1848, this became the chief source for the world, but later this distinction went to Australia, and now belongs to South Africa, which today yields over half the annual supply.

The ultimate source of gold is from the lighter colored igneous rocks, like granites, syenites, and diorites, throughout which it is diffused in quantities too small to be either visible or worth while to extract. It becomes available only when it has been dissolved out by percolating waters and segregated in fissures or veins, either in or leading from these igneous rocks. Generally this transfer of gold has taken place when the rocks were at high temperatures, and by the aid of water (and perhaps other solvents) which was also at high temperatures. The presence of gold in sandstones, limestones, etc., is secondary, as is also its presence in sea water, in which there is reported to be nearly a grain (about five cents worth) in every ton of water. Beside the direct recovery of gold from gold mining, a great deal is obtained from its association with iron, copper, silver, lead and zinc sulphides, in which it is included in particles too fine to be visible, but in quantities large enough to be separated from the other metals after they are smelted.

In the United States gold is found in the Cordilleran region from California to Alaska, in Colorado, Nevada, Arizona, Utah, the Black Hills of South Dakota, and in small quantities in the metamorphosed slates of North and South Carolina, Georgia, and in Nova Scotia.

THE SILVER GROUP

Though much commoner than gold, silver did not attract the eye of man as early, probably because it tarnishes when exposed to air or any other agent having sulphur compounds in it.

and a black film of silver sulphide covers the surface. Its first use was for ornaments, and some of these found in the ruins of ancient Troy indicate its use as early as 2500 B.C. A thousand years later it was being used to make basins, vases and other vessels.

Silver is next to gold in malleability and ductility, so that a grain of silver can be drawn out into a wire 400 feet long, or beaten into leaves $\frac{1}{100000}$ of an inch in thickness. As a conductor of electricity it is unsurpassed, being rated at 100% while copper rates 93%. Silver is also like gold in the freedom with which it alloys with other metals, such as gold, copper, iron, platinum, etc. All our silver coins, tableware, etc., have some copper alloyed with the silver to give it greater hardness and durability

Unlike gold, silver freely enters into compounds with the non-metals, which is the reason that it is not found primarily in its native state, but usually as a sulphide. Its ultimate source is in the igneous rocks, few granites or lavas, on analysis, failing to show at least traces of silver. Before it is available as an ore, or mineral, it has been dissolved from the original magma, and segregated in fissures or veins, along with such minerals, as quartz, fluorite, calcite, etc. This seems to have taken place while the igneous rocks were still hot, and by the agency of vapors and liquids which were also hot. The presence of silver in sedimentary and metamorphic rocks. or even in sea water, is secondary.

The primary deposition of silver is usually in the form of sulphides, the commoner of which are, argentite or silver sulphide, pyrargyrite or silver and antimony sulphide, and prousite, or silver and arsenic sulphide. Its occurrence as native silver, or the chloride, cerargyrite, is secondary and due to the reactions which have taken place when sulphide deposits have been subjected to weathering agents.

The United States produces about 25% of the world's supply, Mexico some 35%. It is especially found along the Cordilleran ranges of both North and South America.

Silver
Ag, Pl.6
Usually non-crystalline, but occasionally showing cube or octahedron faces of the isometric system; hardness 2.5; specific gravity 10.5; color silvery white; luster metallic; opaque.

When found in its native state silver is usually in wirey, flakey, or mossy masses; but sometimes masses of considerable size occur, the most famous being an 800 pound nugget found in Peru, and another of 500 pounds weight found at Konsberg, Norway, and now preserved in Copenhagen. When exposed to the air the surface soon tarnishes and takes on a black color which must be scraped off to see the real color.

Like gold, silver is usually found associated with other metals, like iron, copper, lead and zinc; and much of the silver recovered is obtained in connection with the mining, especially of copper and lead. Some lead ores have so much silver in them that they are better worth mining for the silver; galena, for instance, under such circumstances being termed argentiferous galena. Native silver is a secondary mineral, having been formed by the reduction of some one of its sulphides by water, carrying various elements which had a greater affinity for the sulphur.

Silver is found along with copper in the Lake Superior region, and in Idaho, Nevada, and California.

Argentite
AgS, Pl. 6
silver glance

Usually in irregular masses, but sometimes in cubes; hardness 2.5; specific gravity 7.3; color and streak lead gray; luster metallic; opaque on thin edges.

Argentite, the simple sulphide of silver, is the chief source from which silver is obtained. It looks like galena, and has the same hardness, streak and specific gravity, but can be distinguished by the galena having a very perfect cubic cleavage while the argentite has no cleavage. Argentite is easily cut with a knife (sectile). It is usually found in irregular masses, but sometimes in cubes which make very choice cabinet specimens; and is associated with such other minerals as galena, sphalerite, chalcopyrite, pyrite, fluorite, quartz, and calcite.

It occurs in fissures and veins all through the Cordilleran regions, especially in California, Colorado, Nevada (Comstock Lode), Arizona (Silver King Mine) and about the shores of Lake Superior.

Pyrargyrite
Ag₃SbS₃
Pl. 7
ruby silver or
dark red silver

Usually occurs in irregular masses; hardness 2.5; specific gravity 5.8; color dark red to black; streak purplish red; luster metallic to adamantine; translucent on thin edges.

Pyrargyrite, the sulphide of silver and anti-mony, is distinguished by its dark red color and the purplish streak. It may look like prousite, but is easily distinguished from the latter which has a scarlet streak. It also at times looks like hematite and cinnabar, but the hematite has a hardness of 6, and the latter has the bright red color throughout, while pyrargyrite turns black when exposed to the light, so that the characteristic red color will be seen only on fresh surfaces. The characteristic red color can only be kept on the mineral if it is constantly protected from the light.

Sometimes pyrargyrite occurs in crystals and these belong to the hexagonal system, and are prisms with low faces on the ends, as on plate 7, and the mineral is peculiar in that the faces on the opposite ends are unlike.

Pyrargyrite is found mostly in fissures and veins of quartz, fluorite, calcite, etc., and associated with pyrite, chalcopyrite, galena, etc. It is fairly common in Colorado in Gunnison and Ouray counties, in Nevada, New Mexico, Arizona, etc.

Prousite
$Ag_3 AsS_3$
Pl. 7
light red silver

Usually occurs in irregular masses; hardness 2.5; specific gravity 5.6; color scarlet to vermilion; streak the same; luster adamantine: transparent on thin edges.

In general this mineral is very like pyrargyrite, but has the scarlet color and streak which are entirely characteristic. It is likely to have the surface tarnished black, which happens on exposure to light, so that it is essential to be sure that fresh surfaces are being examined. Occasionally it is found in crystals, of the same type as the preceding mineral. It is generally found associated with pyrargyrite.

Cerargyrite
AgCl
horn silver

Usually found in irregular masses or incrustations; hardness 1 to 1½; specific gravity 5.5; color pearly gray, grayish green to colorless, but turning violet brown on exposure to light; luster resinous; transparent on thin edges.

This mineral is usually found in thin seams or waxy incrustations, but it may occur in crystals in which case they are cubes. It is very soft and easily cut with a knife, which with its tendency to turn violet-brown on exposure to light, makes it easy to identify. Cerargyrite is a secondary mineral, resulting from the action of chlorine-bearing water on some one of the sulphides of silver. It is found in the upper portions of mines, especially those in arid regions.

THE COPPER GROUP

After gold the next metal to be utilized was copper. About 4000 B.C. our early forefathers found that by heating certain rocks, they obtained a metal which could be pounded, ground and carved into useful shapes. Curiously enough the rocks which had the copper also had some tin in them, so that this first-found copper was not pure, but had from five to ten per cent of tin in it, making the resulting metal harder, and what we call bronze. It was some thousands of years later before they distinguished the copper as a pure metal, but it worked and made good tools. The newly found metal was not as ornamental as gold; but, because it could be made into tools, it had a tremendous influence on man's development. As the bronze tools began to take the place of the stone implements, the "Age of Bronze" was ushered in. In America the Indians in the Lake Superior region found native copper weathered out of the rocks and later mined it, and they too pounded it into knives, axes, needles, and ornaments, but probably never learned to melt it and mold their tools. At any rate they were not as far advanced in using this metal when Columbus landed as were the southern Europeans 6500 years earlier. Since the use of iron became general, copper has not held such a dominant place, but it still is "the red metal" which holds the second most important place.

It is malleable and ductile, though not equal to gold or silver in these respects. It is a good conductor of electricity and a very large amount of copper is used in electrical manufacture, roofing, wire, etc. It alloys with other metals; ten parts copper and one of tin being bronze, ten of copper and one of zinc is brass, and copper with aluminum is aluminum bronze.

Like silver and gold, copper is widely diffused through the igneous rocks, but before it is available, it must be leached out by solvents and concentrated in veins, fissures, or definite parts of the lavas or granites. The primary ores are those which, while the igneous rock was still hot, were carried by hot vapors and liquids into the fissures and there deposited, mostly as sulphides. There is a long list of these, but in this country, the following are the commoner ones; chalcocite the sulphide of copper, chalcopyrite the sulphide of copper and iron, bornite another combination of copper, iron and sulphur, and tetrahedrite copper and antimony sulphide. When these primary ores are near enough to the surface to come in contact with waters carrying oxygen, carbon dioxide or silica in solution, they may give up their sulphur and take some one of these new elements and we have such forms as cuprite, the oxide of copper, malachite and azurite, carbonates of copper, or chrysocolla, the silicate of copper. Native copper is also a secondary deposit laid down in its present state by a combination of circumstances which deprived it of its original sulphur. In general copper mining can not be profitably carried on for ores with anything less than a half of one percent in them; and the use of such low grade ores has only been possible for a few years, as the result of inventing most delicate processes in the smelting.

The United States produces about a quarter of the world's supply of copper, with Chile ranking second with about 17%.

Copper
Cu, Pl. 8
Usually in irregular masses; hardness 2.5; specific gravity 8.9; color copper red; luster metallic; opaque.
Native copper, easily determined by its color

and hardness, is generally found in irregular grains, sheets, or masses, on which may sometimes be detected traces of a cube or an octahedral face, showing that it belongs to the isometric system. The most famous locality is the Upper Peninsula of Michigan which may be taken as typical. Here, long before it was known historically, the Indians found and dug out copper to make knives, awls, and ornaments.

In this region, beds of lava alternate with sandstones and conglomerates. The copper was originally in the lavas, but has been dissolved out, and now fills cracks and gas cavities in the lavas, and also the spaces between the pebbles of the conglomerate. This locality has been very famous both because of the quantity mined, and also because of the strikingly large masses sometimes found. Today but little of the ore runs above 2 percent copper, and it is mined if it has as little as ½ of one percent.

While nowhere near as abundant, native copper occurs in the same way in cavities and cracks in the trap rocks of New Jersey, and along the south shore of the Bay of Fundy. It is also known from Oregon, the White River region of Alaska, and in Arctic Canada.

Chalcopyrite Occurs in crystals or irregular
$CuFeS_2$ masses; hardness 4; specific gravity
Pl. 8 4.2; color bronze yellow; streak
copper pyrites greenish black; luster metallic;
or *yellow* opaque on thin edges.
copper ore
Chalcopyrite resembles pyrite, but its color is a more golden yellow, and its surface

tarnishes with iridescent colors. Then too the hardness of chalcopyrite is but 4 as compared with 6 for pyrite. When in crystals this mineral belongs to the tetrahedral system as the c axis is but .985 in length as compared with 1 for the two other axes. This difference is so little; that, to the eye, the octahedron appears to belong to the isometric system. Chalcopyrite occurs in octahedrons and tetrahedrons (as on plate 8), the latter being the form where but half of the octahedral faces are developed. However by far the most frequent mode of occurrence is in irregular masses.

This is the most important primary ore of copper, and is widely distributed, being found either in lavas, or in veins, or in fissures connected with igneous rocks. Apparently the deposits were made, either at the time of eruptive disturbances or shortly afterward, from vapors or hot solutions carrying the copper sulphides (and other sulphides) from the molten igneous rocks. Chalcopyrite is usually associated with pyrite, galena, sphalerite and chalcocite, as well as quartz, fluorite and calcite. It is found in all the New England States, in New York, New Jersey, Pennsylvania, Maryland, Virginia, North Carolina, Tennessee, Missouri, and all the Rocky Mountain and Pacific Coast States.

Bornite
Cu_3FeS_3
purple copper ore — Occurs in granular or compact masses; hardness 3; specific gravity, 5; color bronze-brown with a bluish tarnish; streak gray-black; luster metallic; opaque on thin edges.

Bornite is also known as erubescite, blushing ore, variegated copper, peacock copper, etc., all of which names refer to the highly iridescent tarnish which fresh faces soon take on when exposed to the air. Though usually in masses, it is sometimes found in rough cubes of the isometric system. In this country it is not abundant enough to be used as an ore, but is likely to be found with other ores like chalcopyrite or chalcocite. In the east it has been found at Bristol, Conn., and near Wilkesbarre, Penn., while in the west it may be expected to occur wherever other sulphide minerals of copper are found.

Chalcocite
Cu₂S, Pl. 9
copper glance

Occurs in fine grained compact masses; hardness 2.5; specific gravity 5.7; color dark leaden gray; streak black; luster metallic; opaque on thin edges.

Chalcocite is one of the important ores of copper, especially in Arizona and the Butte District of Montana. It resembles argentite in color and general appearance, but is readily distinguished by being brittle and having a tendency to tarnish to bluish or greenish colors on fresh surfaces. Occasionally it occurs in crystals which are in the orthorhombic system; but the edges of the prism are so beveled that there are six sides and the prism resembles a hexagonal prism (see page 16).

In the Butte, Mont., district, the most important copper region in the United States, fully 50% of the ore is chalcocite, which is a derivative of the originally deposited chalcopyrite, the latter having lost its iron. In the veins of this district chalcopyrite, bournite, tetrahedrite, and several other copper minerals not described in this book, occur all together, and with them also gold, silver and arsenic minerals. The gold amounts to about 2¼ cents per pound of copper, and the silver is in somewhat less quantity. These veins were first opened to get the silver ores, which were the more important ones down to a depth of 200 to 400 feet. Below these depths the copper became much more important. It was the weathering which had removed a large part of the copper minerals in the upper levels of the veins, but had left a large part of the silver. Chalcocite is also important in most of the Utah and Arizona mines.

In the east it has been found at Bristol, Simsbury and Cheshire, Conn., and in the west it is found in all the Cordilleran States.

Tetrahedrite
Cu_3SbS_3
Pl. 9 & 10
gray copper ore

Occurs in irregular masses and in tetrahedrons of the isometric system; hardness 3.5; specific gravity 4.7; streak dark brown; luster metallic; opaque on thin edges.

In its crystalline form the tetrahedrite occurs in tetrahedrons, which generally have faces formed by beveling the edges and by cutting the corners, as in the two figures of plate 10. Chalcopyrite may also occur in tetrahedrons, but its golden yellow color is entirely different from the gray-black of the tetrahedrite. When in masses the hardness and the streak which is dark brown, are very characteristic.

In England and Bolivia tetrahedrite is an important ore of copper, but in this country it is simply a copper mineral which is widely distributed, and associated with most of the mining enterprises, but is in no case the important ore. It has been found sparingly through the New England States, at the Kellogg Mines in Arkansas, and abundantly in Colorado, Montana, Utah, Arizona, Nevada and New Mexico.

Cuprite, Cu₂O Occurs in isometric cubes, octa-
Pl. 9 & 10 hedrons, and dodecahedrons, or in
red copper masses; hardness 3.5; specific grav-
ore ity 6; color dark brownish-red;
streak brownish-red; luster metallic; translucent on thin edges.

When in crystals cuprite is easily determined, but when in masses its fresh surfaces may suggest prousite, but the streak and hardness are quite different in the two cases. Sometimes its color suggests hematite, but the latter has the hardness of 6. When found it is often coated with a thin film of green, which is malachite.

Except when found as native copper, the ore which contains the greatest percentage of copper is cuprite with 88.8% of copper. It is likely to occur in any of the deposits of copper ore, where they are in arid climates and above the level of the underground water, and is very frequently associated with malachite and azurite. In the Bisbee, Arizona, district cuprite is one of the important ores.

Besides the normal occurrence described above, cuprite may be found in two other varieties; one where the crystals have grown side by side and so only the ends have been free for continuous additions of the mineral, which has resulted in a fibrous mass known as "plush copper ore" or chalcotrichite; the other an earthy mixture of limonite and cuprite, which is brick red in color, and termed "tile ore."

Cuprite is found sparingly in New England, more abundantly at such places as Summerville and Flemington, N. J., Cornwall, Penn., in the Lake Superior region, and fairly abundantly in the Cordilleran States.

Malachite
$CuCO_3 \cdot Cu(OH)_2$
Pl. 11

Usually occurs in nodular or incrusting masses; hardness 3.5; specific gravity 4; color green; streak a lighter green; luster adamantine, silky or dull; translucent on thin edges.

The vivid green of malachite is usually enough to determine it at once, but one may be sure by trying a drop of acid on it, in which case it effervesces as is characteristic of so many carbonates, but this is the only carbonate which is vivid green. Generally the malachite is in irregular masses, but crystals are occasionally found. These are extremely small and needle-like, and belong to the monoclinic system. In the Ural Mountains there is a locality where these crystals grow in fibrous masses, usually radiating from the center. Malachite in such nodules has a silky luster. These rare nodules have furnished the rulers of Russia with a unique and much prized material for making royal gifts. In European museums and palaces one finds many objects carved from this form of malachite, and marked as gifts of the czars of Russia.

In the United States malachite is widely distributed, appearing as green streaks and stains where copper minerals have been exposed to the air. It is the green tarnish which appears on bronze and copper when exposed to the weather. It is found in large quantities in New Jersey, Pennsylvania, Wisconsin, Nevada, Arizona, Utah, New Mexico, etc. The Bisbee mine in Arizona is the place that has furnished museums with so many of the handsome specimens of malachite associated with azurite. These are the most striking specimens for the vividness of their colors that appear in any collections.

Malachite has been known since about 4000 B.C., the Egyptians having mines where they obtained it between the Suez and Mt. Sinai. In those early days it was particularly a child's charm, protecting the wearer from evil spirits. It is still used as a stone of lesser value in making some sorts of jewelry.

Azurite
$2CuCo_3 \cdot Cu(OH)_2$
Pl. 11
Occurs as short prismatic or tabular crystals of the monoclinic system; hardness 4; specific gravity 3.8; color azure blue; streak lighter blue; luster vitreous; translucent on thin edges.

Azurite is another very striking mineral fully characterized by its color and streak. Like malachite it effervesces in acid. It is very near to malachite in composition, and by increasing its water content, can and freely does change to the green mineral; so that few specimens of

46

azurite are without traces of malachite. **It is** found in the same places as malachite, but is not as abundant in the east.

Azurite with the accompanying malachite is cut and polished to make semi-precious stones for some forms of jewelry.

Chrysocolla Never occurs in crystals, but in $CuSiO_3 \cdot 2 H_2O$. seams and incrustations; hardness 2–4; specific gravity 2.1; color bluish-green; streak white; luster vitreous; translucent on thin edges.

This rather rare mineral often appears in opal- or enamel-like incrustations, and its color is variable ranging from the typical bluish-green to sky-blue or even turquoise blue. This is a mineral resulting from the action of silica bearing waters, coming in contact with most any of the copper minerals, and is found accompanying cuprite, malachite, azurite, etc. It is never in large enough quantities to be used as an ore, but its striking color attracts attention and it can be found fairly frequently, especially in the west.

THE IRON GROUP

Pure iron is a chemical curiosity which looks very much like silver. As obtained from its ores, or as it occurs in Nature, iron always has some impurities with it, such as carbon, silicon, sulphur and phosphorus, and these are highest in the crudest iron such as "pig-iron." Its malleability and ductility are only a little less than for gold and silver, and so it has a wide range of qualities for use by man. It is only rarely found native in minute grains in some of the dark lavas. There is however one remarkable exception to this statement, in that on Disco Island, Greenland, there is a basaltic rock, from which are weathered great boulders of native iron up to 20 tons in weight. This iron is very like that occurring in meteorites, and probably came from great depths in the earth's interior. The specific gravity of iron is 7.8. It makes up around 5% of the crust of the earth, and probably occurs in much larger percentages in the interior of the earth.

Iron was discovered by man later than gold or silver or copper, about 1000 B.C.; but once found it was so much more abundant than any of these that it soon dominated over copper, and from Roman times to the present has been the basis of progress in civilization, and these times are well called "the iron age."

Iron unites freely with the non-metals, and occurs as sulphides, oxides, carbonates, etc., and is also present as a secondary metal in that great group of minerals known as the silicates (see page 97). It alloys with a wide range of other metals, every combination altering the properties of the iron, and thus making it useful in a still greater range of manufacture. The introduction of $\frac{1}{4}$ to $2\frac{1}{2}$% of carbon into iron makes steel, which is harder (in proportion to the amount of carbon) and stronger than the pure iron.

Iron compounds are among the most numerous and important of the colors in Nature's paint box, limonite furnishing the browns which color the soil and so many of the rocks, hematite giving the red color to other abundant rocks, and magnetite often coloring igneous rocks black.

while the chlorophyll which gives the green color to plants is an iron compound, as is also the hemoglobin which gives the red to our blood.

Iron is present in all igneous rocks, and secondarily in the sedimentary and metamorphic rocks. It is soluble in water, and so is being constantly transferred from place to place, and changes from one compound to another, according to the circumstances in which it is placed.

The primary forms are pyrite, magnetite and the silicates. When in weathered rocks the iron is changed to limonite, siderite or hydrated silicates. Hematite is an intermediate oxide from which the water contained in limonite has been driven off by moderate heat or bacterial action.

Limonite
$2Fe_2O_3 \cdot 3H_2O$
Pl. 12

Never crystalline, occurs in mammillary, botryoidal and stalactitic forms, or in fibrous, compact, oolitic, nodular or earthly masses; hardness 5.5; specific gravity 3.8; color yellow-brown to black; streak yellow-brown; luster metallic to dull; opaque.

Limonite is a very common mineral, the color, streak and hardness identifying it readily. Iron rust is its most familiar form. When powdered it is the ochre yellow used in paints. Being so universally distributed, it is to be expected it will occur in a variety of ways. First, there is the fibrous type found lining cavities, in geodes, or hanging in stalactites in caves. This has a silky luster, an opalescent, glazed or black surface, and is in mammillated or botryoidal masses. Second, it may occur in compact masses in veins, where it was deposited by waters; which, circu-

lating through the adjacent rocks, gathered it
from the rocks, and, on reaching the open seams,
gave it up again. Third, it may occur in beds
on the bottom of ponds, where it was deposited
by waters which gathered it as they flowed over
the surface of the country rocks. Measurements
in Sweden show that it may accumulate in such
places as much as six inches in the course of
twenty years. In ponds and swamps, the decaying vegetation forms organic compounds, which
cause the precipitation of the iron from the water,
as it is brought in by the streams. This sort of
iron in the bottom of ponds or swamps is also
known as "bog iron." Another form in which
limonite may occur in ponds, lakes, or even the
sea, is in oolitic masses. In this case the iron
forms in tiny balls, with perhaps a grain of sand
at the center, and one coat of iron after another
formed around it, like the layers of an onion. If
the resulting balls are tiny this is called oolitic
(like fish eggs), but if the balls are larger it is
pisolitic (like peas). Bacteria probably have a
good deal to do with the precipitation of limonite
in this manner. Fourth, limonite occurs in
earthy masses, usually mixed with impurities
like clay and sand, which are the residue left
behind, where limestones have been dissolved by
weathering. The fifth mode of occurrence is
known as gossan, or "the iron hat," which is a
mass of limonite capping a vein of some sulphide
mineral, like pyrite, chalcopyrite or pyrrhotite,
which has been exposed to weathering; and in
these minerals the sulphur has been removed,
leaving a mass of limonite over the vein. This is

particularly common in the west. Limonite is quite easily fusible and so was probably the first ore from which early man extracted iron.

Limonite is iron oxide, with 3 molecules of water of crystallization (or constitution) associated with every 2 molecules of the oxide. If limonite is moderately heated the water is driven out and the resulting compound is hematite, the same oxide, but without the water. In this case and many other similar cases, as gypsum, opal, etc., we have two or more minerals resulting from the presence or absence of water in the mineral. The water molecules have a definite place in the arrangement of molecules which determines the structure of the mineral. Sometimes the water is driven out at a temperature around 212 F., in which case it is called, water of crystallization, but in other cases as gypsum, a considerably higher temperature is required to drive out the water, and then it is called, water of constitution. In all cases the removal of the water changes the arrangement of molecules and a new mineral results, with characteristics of its own.

In this case limonite is only one of a series of minerals which have the Fe_2O_3 molecule as a basis, and that incorporate more or less water into their molecular construction as follows:

Turgite	$2Fe_2O_3 \cdot H_2O$
Goethite	$Fe_2O_3 \cdot H_2O$
Limonite	$2Fe_2O_3 \cdot 3H_2O$
Xanthosiderite	$Fe_2O_3 \cdot 2H_2O$
Limnite	$Fe_2O_3 \cdot 3H_2O$

Of these goethite is crystalline, the others non-crystalline. They may occur pure or in all sorts of mixtures, the mixtures usually being lumped under limonite. The limonite is far the commonest of the series, goethite is fairly common, but the others are rare as pure minerals.

Limonite is found in all parts of all states and in every country. Though so common, it is by no means an important source of iron today, only about one percent of the iron mined in this country coming from this source, though in Germany, Sweden and Scotland it is relatively much more important.

Goethite Occurs in lustrous brown to black
Fe₂O₃. H₂O orthorhombic prisms, usually ter-
Pl. 12 minated by low pyramids; hardness 5; specific gravity 4; color brown to black; streak brownish-yellow; luster imperfect adamantine; opaque.

Goethite, named for the poet Goethe, who was interested in mineralogy, is much less abundant than limonite or hematite, but occurs with them, when they are in veins. Its usual form is an orthorhombic prism with the edges beveled, and a low pyramid on either end. The crystals usually grow in clusters, making a fibrous mass, often radiated, in which case it is known as "needle iron stone"; or the prisms may be so short as to be almost scales; when, because of the yellowish-red color, it is called "ruby mica." It is found in many states, including Connecticut, Michigan, Colorado, etc.

Hematite
Fe_2O_3
Pl. 13 & 14
specular iron

Occurs in compact, mammillary, botryoidal, or stalactitic masses of dark red to black color, or in earthy masses of bright to dark red; hardness 6; specific gravity 5.2; color ochre red to black; streak cherry red to dark red; luster metallic, vitreous, or dull; opaque on thin edges.

Hematite is readily distinguished from other red minerals by its hardness and streak. It may occur in crystals, which belong to the hexagonal system, and are usually hemihedral forms of the double pyramid, or rhombohedrons. These rhombohedrons usually have the edges beveled, as in Pl. 13, A; or are tabular in form as a result of the beveling of two of the opposite edges to such an extent that a form like Pl. 13 B results. However the usual occurrence is in non-crystalline masses, which represent transformations from limonite by the loss of water of crystallization on the part of the limonite. In such cases we have fibrous, oolitic or compact masses, according to the form in which the limonite occurred. The transformation from limonite into hematite involves some heat to drive out the water of crystallization, but nothing like what is involved in metamorphism.

Hematite is the source of 90% of the iron mined in this country. Part of it comes from the famous Clinton iron ore, a layer a foot or more in thickness; starting in New York State, and extending all down the Appalachian Mountains to Alabama, where it is ten or more feet thick and the basis of the Birmingham iron industries. Then there are tremendous deposits of earthy to compact hematite, probably derived from limonite, around the west end of Lake Superior. This latter region yields today around 75% of the iron for this country.

Loose earthy masses of hematite are often known as "ochre red," and were used by the Indians for war paint. Today the same sort of material is obtained by powdering hematite and using it for red paint. The red color in great stretches of rock is due to the presence of small amounts of hematite, acting as cementing material. The red of the ruby, garnet, spinel, and the pink of feldspars and calcite are due to traces of hematite.

This mineral is very common and found in every state.

Magnetite
Fe_3O_4, Pl. 14
Magnetic iron ore
Occurs in masses or in isometric octahedrons or dodecahedrons; hardness 6; specific gravity 5.8; color black; streak black; luster metallic; opaque on thin edges.

Magnetite is another important ore of iron, and is peculiar in being strongly magnetic; its name being derived, according to Pliny, from that of the shepherd Magnes, who found his iron pointed staff attracted by the mineral when he was wandering on Mount Ida. This magnetic property has been repeatedly used to locate beds of magnetite, and is very helpful in separating magnetite from the "black sands," of which it so often forms a part. These sands however generally have magnetite with so much titanium in it that they are unfit for smelting.

Magnetite is found in association with igneous or metamorphic rocks, and often represents limonite or hematite which has been altered as the result of high temperatures. Some of it, in the igneous rocks especially, was undoubtedly in the molten magma and has crystallized out from the magma while it was still hot. It is the form of iron always indicative of former high temperatures. It is an ore mineral for about 3% of the iron in this country, but in Scandinavia and some other countries, it plays a leading rôle as the source of iron.

It is found in the Adirondack Mountains, in New Jersey, Pennsylvania, Arkansas, North Carolina, New Mexico, and California.

Siderite
$FeCO_3$
Pl. 13 & 14
Spathic iron

Occurs in fibrous botryoidal masses or rhombohedral crystals, sometimes with curved faces; hardness 3.5; specific gravity 3.8; color gray-brown; streak white; luster vitreous; translucent on thin edges.

Like hematite this mineral belongs to the hexagonal system, and crystallizes in hemihedral form, making the rhombohedron. Its faces are often curved, which is rare in minerals, only a few forms like this and dolomite having other than plane faces. When siderite crystals grow in clusters, the crowding often results in growth on one face only, making a mass of fibrous character, and in such cases the surface of the mass is botryoidal in contour. The mineral is likely to oxidize, losing its gray-brown color, and becoming limonite. In the United

States it is scarcely ever used as an ore for iron, but in Germany and England a great deal of iron is smelted from this mineral.

It occurs in Massachusetts, Connecticut, New York, throughout the Appalachian Mountains, and also in Ohio.

Pyrite
FeS_2
Pl. 15 & 16
iron pyrites
Occurs as cubes, octahedrons and pyritohedrons, or in compact masses, scales or grains; hardness 6; specific gravity 5.1; color brassy yellow; streak greenish-black; luster metallic; opaque on thin edges.

This is one of the commonest of all minerals. It is found in all kinds of rocks, with all kinds of associations, in all parts of the world. Its crystals are isometric, and cubes and octahedrons are abundant. The pyritohedron is also a common form, and characteristic of this mineral. It is a hemihedral form derived from a 24-sided form, *i.e.* the cube with four faces on each side. On this 24-sided form each alternate face has developed and the others have disappeared, resulting in a 12-sided form, known as the pyritohedron, which differs from the dodecahedron in that each of its faces is five-sided instead of rhomboidal. When in crystals pyrite can not be easily confused with any other mineral; but when in masses it is often mistaken for gold, chalcopyrite, pyrrhotite or marcasite. From the first two, the color should be sufficient to distinguish it, for they are golden yellow. Pyrrhotite is bronze yellow, and marcasite is paler yellow. Then too in hardness pyrite is

56

much harder than any of these minerals except marcasite. This last is the one which is most likely to cause real difficulty. Its lighter color, and the fact that it usually comes in fibrous masses are the best distinctions.

In spite of being so abundant pyrite is scarcely ever used as an ore for iron, because the sulphur makes the metal "short," or brittle, and the sulphur is not easily gotten entirely out of the iron; but pyrite is used largely in the manufacture of sulphuric acid, so important to many of our industries.

Other sulphides are commonly mixed with pyrite, such as chalcopyrite arsenopyrite, argentite, etc.; but the most important impurity is gold, which is often scattered through the pyrite in invisible particles, and sometimes in quantities enough to make it worth while to smelt it for the gold.

Pyrite is particularly the form in which the sulphur compounds of iron appear in rocks which have been highly heated, and is to be expected in metamorphic rocks and also igneous rocks, especially in fissures and veins leading from the igneous rocks. It may occur in sedimentary rocks, but in these last it is usually marcasite.

Marcasite
FeS_2, Pl. 15
white pyrite
Occurs in orthorhombic crystals, usually grouped to make fibrous or radiating masses, or non-crystalline in masses; hardness 6; specific gravity 4.8; color pale brassy-yellow; streak greenish-gray; luster metallic; opaque on thin edges.

Marcasite has the same chemical composition,

as pyrite, and looks like it, but is lighter colored and usually occurs in fibrous masses. It is the commoner form in limestones and shales, while pyrite is more likely to occur in igneous and metamorphic rocks. It seems probable that marcasite is due to a more hasty precipitation from cold solutions, while pyrite is deposited more slowly from hot solutions.

Isolated crystals of marcasite are rare; but, if formed, they belong to the orthorhombic system. Usually some form of twinning is present, and because of the multiple character of the twinning, marcasite crystals usually show a ragged outline, with reentrant angles. It is most abundant in radiated masses, which appear fibrous on the broken surfaces. It decomposes easily, taking oxygen from the air and forming, even in museum cases, a white efflorescence or "flower," which is iron sulphate or melanterite. In moist air it takes water and decomposes to sulphuric acid which may change the surrounding lime-stone to gypsum. Marcasite is found wherever limestones and shales are the country rock.

Pyrrhotite $Fe_{11}S_{12}$ *Magnetic pyrites*   Occurs in masses; hardness 4: specific gravity 4.6: color bronze; streak grayish-black; luster metallic; opaque on thin edges.

Tabular crystals are known, but are very rare. They belong to the hexagonal system. This form is easily distinguished from the other yellow minerals by being magnetic. It is by no means as abundant as the two preceding sulphides of iron, but does occur fairly frequently in veins in igneous rocks, and less frequently in limestones, large quantities of sulphuric acid being made from a deposit in limestone at Ducktown, Tenn. It will be found in most states. When associated with nickel it is an important source for the latter mineral, as at Sudbury, Canada. Pyrrhotite is very like a substance found in meteorites, known as troilite.

THE LEAD GROUP

After learning how to get iron from the rocks by rude smelting methods, the early peoples tried heating various rocks, and some time around 500 B.C. stumbled upon lead, which is rather easily separated from its ores. This metal was used through Roman times to make pipes, gutters, etc

Lead is a soft metal, fairly malleable, but with little ductility, and still less tensile strength. Though one of the commoner metals, it does not occur as pure metal in Nature. It is diffused in minute quantities through the igneous rocks, and also is found in the sedimentary rocks and in the sea water. Its minerals are few, galena, the sulphide of lead, being the commonest, and at the same time the form in which lead is primarily deposited. Galena may also represent a secondary deposition. The other minerals, cerrusite, anglesite, and pyromorphite are results of modification of the galena when it lies near enough to the surface to be acted on by weathering agents, like water and air. Lead minerals are usually associated with zinc minerals, there being but few places where the minerals of the one group occur without the other. Most lead when first smelted from its ore, contains a greater or less amount of silver in it, sometimes enough so that the lead ore is better worth working for the silver than for the lead.

Lead is used in making pipes, gutters, bullets, etc., and in its oxide forms in the manufacture of paints and glass. Eighty-three parts of lead with 17 parts of antimony make type metal. Lead and tin alloy to make solder. Lead and tin with small amounts of copper, zinc and antimony make pewter. The United States produce about 20% of the world's supply of this metal.

Galena
PbS, Pl. 17
lead glance
Occurs in cubes or cleavable masses; hardness 2.5; specific gravity 7.5; color lead-gray; streak lead-gray; luster metallic; opaque.

While there is quite a group of lead-gray minerals, galena is easily identified by its cleavage, which is perfect in three directions parallel to the cube faces. Even a moderate blow of the hammer will shatter a mass of galena into small cubic pieces. The crystals often have the corners cut by octahedral faces, and occasionally the edges are beveled by dodecahedral faces. It is not uncommon to find crystals of large size, several inches across. If galena has 1 to 2% of bismuth as an impurity, curiously enough, the cleavage changes to octahedral, but this is a rare occurrence.

Galena may occur as a primary mineral in veins associated with igneous intrusions, or in irregular masses in metamorphic rocks; but it is more often found in irregular masses in limestones, where the limestone has been dissolved, and the cavities thus formed, filled with secondary deposits of galena. It also occurs at the contact between igneous rocks and the adjacent rock, whatever this may be. Sometimes it is found in residual clays.

Among the most important lead deposits are the Cœur d'Alene district in Idaho, where galena with a high percentage of silver is mined; the Leadville, Colo., district where lead, silver and gold occur together in veins; the Joplin, Mo., district, where lead and zinc ores occur together in irregular masses in limestones; and the Wisconsin district of similar character.

When found galena is usually associated with sphalerite, argentite chalcopyrite, pyrite and calcite. It will be found in every state.

Cerrusite Occurs in fibrous or compact
$PbCO_3$, **Pl. 18** masses, or in orthorhombic crystals.
White lead usually on galena; hardness 3.5;
ore specific gravity 6.5; colorless; streak white; luster adamantine; transparent on thin edges.

While the crystals of this mineral simulate hexagonal, they are actually orthorhombic, the simple form being an octahedron with two of its edges beveled, making double six-sided pyramids (see Pl. 18 A.) Usually prism faces are present. Twinning is common, both the simple contact sort, as shown on Plate 18 B, and also the sort in which three crystals have grown through each other, so as to make a six-rayed crystal. The considerable weight, and the fact that it effervesces in acid serve to identify cerrusite. When pure it is colorless, but impurities cause it to appear white, gray or grayish-black, and sometimes it has a tinge of blue or green.

It is likely to occur wherever galena is found, as a secondary mineral derived from the galena. In this country it is not used as an ore, for, as in the Leadville district, veins which have cerrusite near the surface change at moderate depths, and galena takes the place of the cerrusite. It is found all down the Appalachian Mountains, and in all the Cordilleran States. Especially fine specimens have come from the Cœur d'Alene district in Idaho.

Anglesite
PbSO₄, Pl. 18
Occurs in grains and masses, or in tabular and prismatic orthorhombic crystals; hardness 3; specific gravity 6.3; colorless; luster adamantine; transparent on thin edges.

Two modes of occurrence are characteristic, one in cavities in galena, the other in concentric layers around a nucleus of galena. In the former case fine crystals are developed, in the latter the mineral is in masses. The crystals look like those of barite, but are soluble in nitric acid while the barite is insoluble. Sometimes the crystals are prismatic with pyramidal faces instead of the tabular form.

It is found in the lead mines associated with galena, and in this country is not used as an ore for lead, but in Mexico and Australia it is abundant enough to be mined as an ore. Exposed to water which has carbon dioxide in it, and most surface waters have some, it readily changes to cerrusite. It is found in Missouri, Wisconsin, Kansas, Colorado, and Mexico.

Pyromorphite Occurs in small barrel-shaped $Pb_5Cl(PO_4)_3$ hexagonal crystals, and in fibrous or **Pl. 17** earthly masses; hardness 3.5; speci- *Green lead ore* fic gravity 7; color green to brown; luster resinous; translucent on thin edges.

Pyromorphite is found in the upper levels of lead mines, and is formed by the decomposition of galena. Its green color (sometimes shading off toward brown), considerable weight and resinous luster, serve to distinguish this mineral. The crystal form is that of a simple hexagonal prism, with the ends truncated. It is found in Phœnixville, Penn., Missouri, Wisconsin, Colorado, New Mexico, etc.

THE ZINC GROUP

Zinc and copper made the brass of early Roman times; but even then, zinc was not known as a separate metal, the brass being made by smelting rocks in which both zinc and copper occurred, the zinc never being isolated until much later. Some time in the later Roman times it seems to have been obtained separately, but then and all down through the Middle Ages zinc and bismuth were confused. Our earliest record of zinc being smelted, as we know it today, was about 1730 in England. In those earlier days, the product, zinc, or bismuth, or both together, were known as "spelter," and this name has clung to zinc in mining and commercial circles; so that today, if one looks for quotations in the newspaper, he often finds zinc under the head of spelter.

Zinc, like lead, is diffused in small quantities through all the igneous rocks. In places it is segregated in fissures or veins leading from the igneous rocks, along the contact between igneous rocks and either sedimentary or metamorphic rocks, in limestones where solution cavities have been formed and later filled with zinc minerals, and as a residue where limestones have been weathered away. In all these places it is closely associated with lead.

The sulphide, sphalerite, is the primary mineral, and the other minerals, like zincite, smithsonite, calamine, willemite, franklinite, etc., are secondary, resulting from modifications of the original sphalerite. In connection with zinc minerals the region of Franklin Furnace, N. J., is especially interesting, for at that place are found two large metamorphosed deposits containing a wide range of zinc minerals, several of which are not found anywhere else.

Zinc is soft and malleable, but is only slightly ductile, and has little tensile strength. It alloys with several metals, and in this form is most useful today; three parts of copper to one of zinc making brass; four or more parts of copper and one of zinc, making "gold foil"; copper and zinc (a little more zinc than copper) making "white metal": three parts of copper to one of zinc and one of nickel making German silver; etc. Zinc is also used in large quantities in galvanizing iron, sheets of iron being dipped into melted zinc and thus thinly coated. It is also used in batteries and a wide range of chemical industries.

Sphalerite
ZnS,
Pl. 19 & 20
zinc blende,
black jack

Occurs in grains, in fibrous or layered masses, or in isometric crystals; hardness 3.5; specific gravity 4; color yellow-brown to almost black; streak light yellow to brownish luster resinous to adamantine; translucent on thin edges.

When in crystals sphalerite occurs most commonly either in dodecahedrons or in tetrahedrons (hemihedral forms of the isometric octahedron). The cleavage is fairly good and parallel to the faces of the dodecahedron. The difficulty usually is to get large enough crystalline masses to see this cleavage clearly, but by examining the angles between the faces of cleavage pieces they will be found to be the same as those on a dodecahedron. When the mineral is pure, it has the color of resin, but sometimes it is reddish to red-brown, and then it is called "ruby zinc," more often it is dark brown due to the presence of iron as an impurity. This is what the miners call "black-jack." The presence of iron also tends to make the streak darker. The hardness, streak and cleavage will usually determine this mineral readily.

Sphalerite is the primary ore of zinc and is usually found in fissures and veins leading from masses of igneous rocks, or along the surface of contact where igneous rocks like granite or lavas, come against such metamorphic rocks as gneisses, schists, or crystalline limestones. In the region of Joplin, Mo., however, the sphalerite is of secondary character, having been gathered by waters circulating through the limestones, and deposited in them in irregular pockets. This Joplin district has produced more zinc than any other in the world. The United States annually produces about 25% of the world's supply of this metal.

Sphalerite is always associated with galena, and such other minerals as argentite, pyrite, chalcopyrite, fluorite, quartz, calcite and barite, are very apt to be present. It will be found in almost every state, especially in fissures and veins, and less frequently in cavities in limestones.

Zincite
ZnO
Pl. 19 & 20
red zinc ore
Usually occurs massive, but may be found in crystals; hardness 4: specific gravity 5.6; color deep red: streak orange; luster subadamantine: translucent on thin edges.

When in crystals zincite forms in hexagonal prisms with hexagonal pyramids on the ends. This is rather rare, most of the zincite being found in massive form. The cleavage is parallel to the prism faces and perfect. The deep red color and orange streak are wholly characteristic.

This mineral is so common at Franklin Furnace, N. J., as to be an important ore, but it is very seldom found elsewhere. This district, as mentioned before, is a peculiar one for zinc minerals. The zinc beds are in a metamorphosed limestone, and into this are intruded numerous dikes of granite. Probably the zinc was originally present in the bed of limestone as smithsonite, calamine and other secondary minerals of zinc. When intruded by the hot granite the smithsonite (carbonate) may well have been altered to the oxide, zincite; while the calamine (hydrous silicate) became the simple silicate, willemite.

Willemite
$ZnSiO_4$
Pl. 20
Occurs in masses or in crystals; hardness 5.5; specific gravity 4.1; color pale yellow when pure; luster resinous; translucent on thin edges.

Willemite is another of the minerals which are distinctively characteristic of Franklin Furnace, and found elsewhere very rarely. It is so common there as to be one of the principal ores, and mostly occurs in irregular masses, but is also found in crystals. These are hexagonal prisms, with a three-sided (rhombohedral) pyramid on the ends. The color when pure is whitish or greenish-yellow, but with small amounts of impurities it may be flesh-red, grayish-white or yellowish-brown. When in crystals it is easily determined; but when massive it looks like calamine, and can only be distinguished by placing a bit of the mineral in a closed tube and heating it, in which case calamine will give off water vapor, while willemite will not.

This mineral is one of those resulting from metamorphic alteration and is derived from calamine, when the latter loses its water of crystallization. It is common at Franklin Furnace, N. J., and also found occasionally elsewhere, as at Salida, Colo., and in Socorro Co., New Mexico.

Calamine
$Zn_2 (OH)_2 \cdot SiO_3$
Occurs as crystalline linings in cavities, or as botryoidal or stalactitic masses; hardness 5; specific gravity 3.4; colorless to white; luster vitreous.

Calamine resembles both smithsonite and willemite when in non-crystalline masses. From the smithsonite it is easily separated by the fact that in nitric acid the smithsonite effervesces and the calamine does not. From willemite it is harder to distinguish, but a piece may be placed in a closed tube and heated. If it is calamine water vapor will be given off, if willemite nothing happens. When calamine occurs in crystals these are orthorhombic and mostly tabular, and the crystals are peculiar in that the two ends are terminated differently.

Both this and smithsonite are secondary minerals and usually occur together when zinc is found in limestones. It is abundant at Franklin Furnace and Sterling Hill, N. J., and also found at Phœnixville, Penn., in Wythe Co., Va., and Granby, Mo.

Smithsonite
$ZnCO_3$
Pl. 21
Dry bone
Usually occurs as incrustations, grains, earthy or compact masses, and as crystals; hardness 5; specific gravity 4.4; color white, yellow, greenish or bluish; streak white; luster vitreous; transparent on thin edges.

When pure this mineral is colorless, but, as **it** occurs, it is usually white, or tinged with some shade of yellow, green, or blue, but in all cases its streak is white. The crystals are rhombohedrons often with edges beveled or corners cut by other faces. It resembles calamine and willemite, but is readily separated from either of these by the acid test, for smithsonite effervesces when acid is placed on it.

Next to sphalerite, smithsonite is the commonest of the zinc minerals. It is a secondary mineral, resulting from the action of lime-charged water acting on sphalerite, and so is likely to be found wherever zinc minerals occur in a limestone region. In the Wisconsin-Illinois-Iowa district it serves as a minor ore of zinc, and is termed here "dry bone." It is also found in the Missouri and Arkansas districts, and in Europe is an important ore for zinc.

Franklinite Occurs in compact grains or $(ZnMn)Fe_2O_4$ masses, and in isometric octahedrons; hardness 6; specific gravity Pl. 21 5; color black; streak reddish-brown; luster metallic; opaque on thin edges.

This is a mineral peculiar to the Franklin Furnace region, from which it gets its name. It looks like magnetite, but its reddish-brown streak and lack of magnetism distinguish it. When it occurs in octahedrons, the edges are rounded, while those of magnetite are sharp. It is a complex and variable oxide of zinc, iron and manganese, which has resulted from the metamorphism of the beds in which it occurred probably being originally something quite different.

THE MANGANESE GROUP

Though manganese was known in the mineral pyrolusite in early times, it was then thought to be magnetite or magnetic iron ore. It was not until 1774 that it was isolated and recognized as a distinct element.

Manganese is one of the lesser elements in the crust of the earth, making less than .07 of one percent, but as an alloy with other metals, especially iron, it has attained a considerable importance to man. It is used chiefly with iron, 20% of manganese making the alloy, spiegeleisen, a combination which occurs in Nature in Germany, and from 20% to 80% making ferromanganese. These alloys are in great demand because they make an especially tough steel essential in the manufacture of munitions. The sources for manganese are the oxide ores, manganite, pyrolusite and psilomelane, which have been formed as secondary minerals, as a result of the weathering of silicates which carry manganese. They occur widely enough, but throughout the United States the deposits are small, and this is one of the elements in which this country is not self-sufficient. The largest producer of manganese is Russia; however she consumes almost all of her output at home, and our supply comes from the next largest producers, India, the Union of South Africa, and the Gold Coast. A shift in trade may be expected when Brazil's recently discovered ore body in Matto Grosso is brought into full production. Besides being used as an alloy, manganese is employed in making paints and dyes, for clearing glass, and for some types of electric batteries.

Pyrolusite
MnO₂

Occurs in earthy or fibrous masses; hardness 1–2; specific gravity 4.8; color black; streak black; luster dull; opaque.

Pyrolusite occurs in soft masses and incrustations, usually leaving a sooty mark on the fingers. Sometimes it seems to be in crystals, but these are pseudomorphs which have the form of manganite, from which the pyrolusite has formed as a result of the water having been driven from the manganite. Frequently pyromorphite and manganite will be found together, and in some cases the outer part of a mass or crystal will be pyrolusite, while the center is still manganite. Psilomelane is another oxide of manganese with water and may appear very like pyrolusite, but both manganite and psilomelane have much greater hardness than does pyrolusite. If there is difficulty in deciding about pyrolusite, it may be placed in a closed tube and heated. It will not be affected by the heat, while, under the same circumstances, both manganite and psilomelane will give off water vapor.

Pyrolusite usually occurs in black streaks or pockets in residual clays which have formed as a result of the decomposition of limestones. It may also occur in dendritic forms in seams and crevices (see manganite). It is found in Vermont, Massachusetts, Virginia, Arkansas, Colorado, California, etc.

Psilomelane
$MnO_2 \cdot H_2O$
Occurs in compact botryoidal or stalactitic masses; hardness 5–6; specific gravity 4.2; color black; streak brownish-black; luster metallic; opaque on thin edges.

Psilomelane is very like pyrolusite, and often occurs with it. It is distinguished by its greater hardness, and the fact, that when heated in a closed tube, it gives off water vapor. From manganite it is more easily distinguished, for it never occurs in crystals, while the manganite is usually crystalline. This and pyrolusite are the principal ores of manganese.

Wad is an impure form of psilomelane, having some iron oxide mixed with the manganese oxide, usually limonite; or the impurity may take the form of a copper, cobalt, lithium or barium oxide.

Psilomelane is found at Brandon, Vt. in Arkansas, Colorado, California, etc.

Manganite
$Mn_2O_3 \cdot H_2O$
Pl. 22
Occurs in prismatic crystals, or in columnar or fibrous masses; hardness 4; specific gravity 4.4; color steel gray; streak reddish-black; luster submetallic; opaque on thin edges.

This is the form taken by manganese oxide when it crystallizes in the presence of moisture, and pyrolusite frequently changes to manganite when exposed to moisture. The crystals are orthorhombic prisms, with striated sides and the ends truncated. These prisms usually occur in bundles and give the mineral a fibrous appearance. Manganite is not hard to identify, the striations on the crystals and the streak being very characteristic.

In seams and tiny crevices this mineral, and often pyrolusite, grows in a branching manner, resembling tree-like or "mossy" masses. This is termed dendritic, and the growths of manganese minerals are called dendrites. One of the most curious of these is when the "mossy" growth is inclosed in chalcedony, making the so-called *moss agate*. These moss agates are abundant through the Rocky Mountains and are frequently cut for semi-precious stones. The finest ones however come from India and China.

Manganite is found in the Lake Superior region, Colorado, etc.

Rhodochrosite
$MnCO_3$
Occurs in compact cleavable masses; hardness 4; specific gravity 3.5; color rose to dark red; streak white; luster vitreous; translucent on thin edges.

This usually occurs in pink to red masses which cleave readily parallel to the faces of the rhombohedron. When it is found in crystals, which are rare, these too are rhombohedrons. It is usually found in veins as a gangue mineral with copper, silver or zinc ores. Its beautiful color and the fact that it effervesces in acid serve to distinguish this mineral. It is found at Branchville, Conn., at Franklin Furnace, N. J., and in veins with silver in Colorado, Nevada, and Montana.

THE ALUMINUM GROUP

Though aluminum is one of the most abundant of all the metals, making some 8% of the crust of the earth, its union with other elements is so firm, that only recently have methods been found for getting the metal free. It was first isolated in 1846, but up to 1890 the extraction of aluminum was so expensive, that it could not be widely used. About that time electrical processes were applied to its extraction, and since then the price has steadily dropped, until now it is under $.20 per pound. It is very malleable, and ductile, and has high tensile strength. Exposed to the air, water or ordinary gases, it does not tarnish; and it is very light, an equal bulk weighing about a third as much as iron. The combination of lightness and strength, and the fact that it is a good conductor of electricity, have made it available for a wide range of uses, such as electrical apparatus, delicate instruments, boats, aeroplanes, and domestic utensils.

It is an essential component of all the important rocks, except sandstone and limestone, and combines to a greater or less degree in a host of minerals. Though present in clays, shales, argillites, feldspars, and micas, it is only from bauxite that it has been successfully extracted. Aside from the small number of simple compounds of aluminum grouped here, it also takes a part in the make-up of a large series of minerals termed silicates, treated a little further on in this book.

It alloys with other metals, especially copper. The union of copper and a small amount of aluminum makes aluminum-bronze, which looks like gold and is used for watch chains, pencil-cases, etc., and also for the antifriction bearings of heavy machinery. A small amount added to steel prevents air holes and cracks in casting.

Corundum
Al_2O_3, Pl. 23

Occurs in cleavable masses or in hexagonal crystals; hardness 9; specific gravity 4; colorless, red, yellow, blue, or gray; luster vitreous to adamantine; translucent to transparent on thin edges.

Corundum is readily recognized by its hardness, second only to that of the diamond. The crystals may be simple six-sided prisms, hexagonal pyramids or combinations of the two. The cleavage is usually described as parting, for it is by no means perfect, but when it is recognizable it is parallel to the faces of a rhombohedron, and cleavage pieces may appear almost cubic.

When in clear and perfect crystals this mineral is one of the most highly prized of all the gems. Clear and colorless it is known as the "*Oriental white sapphire*"; when tinged with blue it is the *sapphire;* when colored yellow, the "*Oriental topaz*"; when green, the "*Oriental emerald*"; when purple, the "*Oriental amethyst*" and when red, the *ruby.* Sapphires range from colorless to deep blue, the value depending on the shade of the blue, and increasing as the color deepens. The Oriental topaz can easily be confused with the true topaz, which is a much commoner and less valuable gem, but can be distinguished by the hardness, topaz having a hardness of but 8. The name emerald is applied to several green gems, mostly to beryl, which is not so hard and is the true emerald. The Oriental emeralds have a value about the same as diamonds. Rubies of clear and deep color are the rarest of all gems, ranging in value about three times as high as diamonds of equal size. The most sought-for shade is the so-called "pigeon-blood red," and the value of a stone of this sort is almost dependent on the whim of the buyer. The best of the rubies come from granites or metamorphosed limestones in Burma; the best sapphires from Ceylon, though both of these, and some of the other corundums of gem quality, have been found in North Carolina and Montana.

Around these stones, which have been used so long among the Hindus, Persians, Jews, Egyptians, and Christians, a wealth of lore has been woven. The sapphire was Saturn's stone, and a talisman to attract Divine favor. Where tradition makes the stone on which the ten commandments were written the sapphire, it is probable that, what was really meant, is lapis lazuli, as is also the case when sapphires are mentioned as building stones for the celestial gates. The ruby in ancient lore is termed "lord of stones," "gem of gems" etc., and so protected its wearer that he was safe from injury in peace or war.

When corundum is colored brown by impurities of iron, it is termed *corundum,* when black by greater quantities of iron, it is *emery.* These varieties are far the commonest form in which corundum occurs, and when ground to finer or coarser powder make the commercial emery. Emery is likely to be found in sands, making so-called "black sands," where it has accumulated as a result of the weathering to bits corundum-bearing rocks. In some one of its forms, corundum is found in Massachusetts, Connecticut, New York, New Jersey, and all down the Appalachian Mountains, also in Colorado, Montana, California, etc.

Bauxite
$Al_2O_3 \cdot 2H_2O$

Occurs in grains, or oolitic or clay-like masses; hardness 1–3; specific gravity 2.5; color white to yellowish-white or reddish-brown.

Bauxite never comes in crystals, but is usually in earthy masses, which have resulted from the decomposition of granitic or volcanic rocks, in circumstances where hot alkaline waters were present. This explanation seems to apply especially to the deposits in France, which were first the chief source of the bauxite, and may be applicable to those in Georgia and Alabama. Some of the other deposits, however, do not seem to have had any hot water available, and the deposit appears more like simple decomposition of the underlying rocks by alkaline waters.

In many cases bauxite resembles limonite in being a mixture of two or more aluminum oxides with water of crystallization, such as $Al_2O_3 \cdot H_2O$, $Al_2O_3 \cdot 2H_2O$ and $Al_2O_3 \cdot 3H_2O$. This is particularly true of the bauxite which resulted from the decomposition of rocks by surface water.

Bauxite is the ore from which aluminum is obtained. The deposits are not large, but the United States has its share of them. It is found in Alabama, Arkansas, Georgia, Missouri, Tennessee, and California.

Cryolite
$Na_3 AlF_6$
Ice stone

Occurs in pseudo-cubic crystals or massive; hardness 2.5; specific gravity 3; color white; luster vitreous; transparent on thin edges.

Cryolite is a relatively soft mineral, colorless to white as snow; for which reason, and partly also because it comes mostly from Greenland it is called "ice stone." It is really monoclinic but the inclination of the c axis is so slight, that unless examined carefully, the crystals appear to be cubic. Until about 1900 great quantities of this mineral were shipped from West Greenland, and from them the metal aluminum was extracted. When bauxite was discovered, it was found to be considerably cheaper to make the aluminum from that mineral, and now cryolite is no longer sought. Aside from its occurrence in Greenland some cryolite is found in Colorado, near Pike's Peak.

THE ARSENIC GROUP

The metal, arsenic, is a dark steel gray in color, when the surface is fresh, but it soon tarnishes. It is very brittle and easily powdered under the hammer, and its only use as a metal, is for an alloy with lead in making shot. Its compounds find a wider use. The white powder called "arsenic" is arsenous acid, and is used mostly in making poisons, which fortunately are easily detected in animal tissues. Copper arsenate, (*Scheele's green*) is a pigment used in making green paint, and formerly in the green colors of wall paper. A combination of arsenous acid, copper oxide and acetic acid is the well known *Paris Green*, so much used for an insecticide. Beside these uses, arsenic serves a large number of other purposes, as in making glass and enamel, embalming fluids, and various medicines.

Curiously arsenic plays a double part, acting part of the time as a metal, as in the two following minerals, and part of the time as a non-metal, as in cobaltite, niccolite, etc

Arsenopyrite Occurs in well formed crystals, grains, or masses; hardness 5.5; **FeAsS, Pl. 24** specific gravity 6; color silver-white; streak black; luster metallic; opaque on thin edges.

When in crystals, they are usually short prisms of the orthorhombic system, either end being terminated with a low roof. Though usually described as silver-white in color, there is always a brassy cast to the color. Its appearance is much like cobaltite and smaltite, but it can be easily distinguished from both these by putting a piece in nitric acid. The arsenopyrite will not materially change the color of the fluid, but the other two turn it rose-red, and all give off the smell of sulphur. It looks sometimes like marcasite, but that is yellower, and has the fibrous structure, not found in arsenopyrite.

It is found in veins or in metamorphic rocks, associated with argentite, galena, sphalerite, chalcopyrite and pyrite. It is distinctly a mineral formed by deposition from hot vapors or hot water rising from either lavas, or in the course of metamorphism.

It is found in New Hampshire, Vermont,

Massachusetts, Connecticut, New York, New Jersey, California, etc.

Realgar
AsS, Pl. 24
Occurs in incrustations or scattered grains; hardness 1.5 to 2; specific gravity 3.5; color orange; streak orange; luster resinous; opaque on thin edges.

Crystals are very rare, but when found are short monoclinic prisms. The color is aurorared, changing to orange as soon as it is exposed to the air. This and the streak are entirely characteristic. It is a mineral associated with hot vapors or hot waters, and is found about volcanoes, as deposits from the hot water of the geysers in Norris Basin, Yellowstone Park, and in veins, associated with barite, stibnite, quartz, etc., as in Massachusetts, Utah, California, etc.

Orpiment
As₂S₃
Occurs as incrustations or powdery masses; hardness 1 to 2; specific gravity 3.5; color lemon yellow; streak yellow; luster resinous.

This mineral is very like realgar in its physical properties, and likely to occur with it. It gives the lemon yellow color to the basins about hot springs, as in the Yellowstone Park, and about volcanoes. It also comes in veins with realgar.

MOLYBDENUM

Molybdenum is a rare metal, silvery-white in color, brittle and very difficult to fuse. It is used mostly as an alloy of steel, to make certain grades of tool steel. The world's greatest supply is obtained from Climax, Colorado, where the principal ore mineral is molybdenite.

Molybdenite
MoS₂ — Occurs in scales or scaly masses, occasionally in tabular hexagonal crystals; hardness 1.5; specific gravity 4.7; color lead-gray; streak bluish-gray; luster metallic; opaque.

This mineral is the chief source for the metal molybdenum. Its extreme softness and greasy feel will distinguish it at once from any other mineral except graphite, which has much the same qualities, but its scaly character and the more bluish tinge in streak and color will distinguish these two.

It occurs in granites, gneisses, and metamorphic rocks in Colorado, New Mexico, Maine, Connecticut, New Hampshire, New York, Pennsylvania, etc.

ANTIMONY

Antimony is another hard, brittle metal, of bluish-white color. Exposed to the air at ordinary temperatures it does not tarnish; and this combined with its hardness make it useful for such alloys as Britannia metal, type metal, and pewter. Only one of its minerals, stibnite, is common enough for mention.

Stibnite
Sb₂S₃
Pl. 25
gray
antimony — Occurs in prismatic or needle-like crystals; hardness 2; specific gravity 4.5; color lead-gray; streak lead-gray; luster metallic; opaque.

The crystals of stibnite are orthorhombic and usually elongated, the sides striated and the ends with low pyramids on them. Sometimes the long crystals are curved or even twisted. There is a well-developed cleavage parallel to face b in the figure. While the color is similar to that of galena, the form and cleavage are so different that stibnite is easily determined.

The ancients used stibnite to color their eyebrows, now it is the source for the metal antimony. Hungary and Japan are famous for the fine large crystals they produce; but moderate sized crystals may be found in this country. It occurs in veins along with pyrite, galena, cinnabar, and realgar, with quartz, calcite or barite as gangue minerals.

Stibnite has been found in Arkansas, California, Nevada, and Utah.

THE NICKEL GROUP

Nickel as a metal is silvery-white in color, rather hard, and does not tarnish when exposed to the air. When pure it is malleable and fairly ductile. It is highly useful for plating other metals to protect their surfaces. Alloyed with steel, it makes a product of extreme hardness. Copper, zinc, and nickel make the well known German silver.

Nickel has a fairly large range of minerals, but they do not occur with any abundance in the United States, so that we have to import most all of our nickel. In the earlier days New Caledonia produced most of the world's supply, but recently since the finding of large nickel deposits near Sudbury, Canada, this locality has not only outstripped New Caledonia, but now produces four-fifths of the world's supply. In this country but two nickel minerals will be found at all common.

Niccolite Occurs in masses; hardness 5.5;
NiAs, Pl. 25 specific gravity 7.4; color pale cop-
copper nickel pery-yellow; streak pale brownish-black; luster metallic; opaque on thin edges.

Niccolite is very seldom in crystals, but if they do occur they are hexagonal. The mineral looks a little like smaltite, but in case there is any question of the determination, dissolve a piece in nitric acid, and if niccolite, it will color the solution green.

Niccolite is usually associated with copper and silver ores, and in this country has been found at Chatham, Conn., and Silver Cliff, Colo. It may be associated with pentlandite, a sulphide of iron and nickel, which is similar in appearance, but not so hard, and occurs in small grains throughout dark lavas. The particles of pentlandite are however so small, that they are seldom noticeable, but at Sudbury, Canada, this is the chief ore of nickel.

Millerite Occurs in needle-like or fibrous
NiS, crystals; hardness 3.5; specific grav-
capillary ity 5.5; color brass-yellow; streak
pyrites greenish black; luster metallic;
opaque on thin edges.

The fibrous crystals of millerite belong to the orthorhombic system. The color and streak suggest pyrite, but the crystals are long and slender, while pyrite is in cubes, octahedrons, etc. If there is any doubt of the identity of this form, place a piece in nitric acid, and if it is millerite, it will color the acid green.

It may occur in veins associated with cobalt and silver minerals, or as a secondary mineral as at Gap Mine, Penn., or in cavities in sedimentary rocks. In the last case it usually is in needle-like crystals growing through calcite crystals, as at St. Louis, Mo., Keokuk, Iowa, and Antwerp, N. Y.

THE COBALT GROUP

As a metal, cobalt is hard, brittle, and of a grayish color, tinged with red. It was not recognized as a separate element until 1735, and even today is one of the minor metals. Cobalt, chromium and a little tungsten make the alloy stellite, which has come into large use in making high-speed tools. The oxide of cobalt (CoO) is "smalt," used to give the blue color to porcelain, pottery, glass, tiles, etc. Invisible ink is made by diluting cobalt chloride in a large quantity of water. This solution is a faint pink color and practically invisible on paper, but if heated it loses water and turns blue in color, and is perfectly visible.

Cobalt is another of the metals, of which the United States does not have an adequate supply. Sweden, Norway and India were the chief sources of supply until cobalt was found near the town of Cobalt in Ontario, Canada, and now this district furnishes 90% of the world's supply.

Cobaltite Usually crystalline in cubes, pyri-
CoAsS tohedrons or octahedrons; hardness
Pl. 26 5.5; specific gravity 6.1; color reddish
cobalt glance silver-white; streak grayish-black;
luster metallic; opaque on thin edges.

In color cobaltite may appear very like arsenopyrite, especially if the reddish tinge is not
strong, in which case the mineral can be definitely determined by putting a piece in nitric
acid. If it is cobaltite the solution will be
colored rose-red, if arsenopyrite there will be no
change of color. The forms of the crystals are
the same as those of pyrite, but the color will
easily distinguish cobaltite from pyrite. This
pink color is characteristically present either in
or about cobalt minerals, being sometimes called
"cobalt bloom." It is a cobalt-arsenic-oxide
with water of crystallization ($Co_3 As_2 O_8 \cdot 8H_2 O$),
which results from the exposure of cobalt and
arsenic minerals to air and moisture. It is the
pink color on the figures of both cobaltite and
smaltite. In Sweden, Norway and India, this is
the chief ore for cobalt, but in the United States
it is rather rare, but is found in Oregon, and at
Cobalt, Canada.

Smaltite Usually occurs in masses; hard-
(CoNi)As₂ ness 5.5; specific gravity 6.2; color
Pl. 26 tin-white to steel-gray; streak gray-
gray cobalt ish-black; luster metallic; opaque
ore on thin edges.

While very like cobaltite, smaltite is almost
never found in crystals, but when crystals are
found, they are cubes. The color is tin-white

but there is usually a pink tinge visible due to the presence of small amounts of "cobalt bloom." If in any doubt about the determination of this mineral, put a piece in nitric acid. If it colors the acid rose-pink, and is non-crystalline it is pretty surely smaltite; if the acid is not affected it is arsenopyrite.

Smaltite is found in Kentucky, Missouri, Colorado, Idaho, California, and at Cobalt in Canada.

CHROMIUM

This metal gets its name in recognition of the many colors (*chroma* "color"), in which its compounds appear. Chromic oxide is a vivid green, used to color porcelains, pottery, tiles, etc., and also as a substitute for the arsenical greens formerly used in wall-paper. The chromate of lead is the pigment, well known to artists as "chrome yellow," and the bichromate of potassium is bright red. The metal is obtained in at least two different forms; one hard, brittle and so resistant to heat as to be infusible at temperatures which would volatilize platinum; the other as a powder which burns brightly if heated in air. While used in paints, dyes, etc., its greatest importance is for the making of ferro-chrome steel, which is used where resistance to sudden shock is required, as in armor plate, automobile springs, ball bearings, etc. With tungsten and cobalt it makes the alloy, stellite, as noted above.

Chromium was used in relatively small quanti-

ties before the first world war, and we imported
our supplies from Turkey, India, New Caledonia,
and Rhodesia. During the last war we started a
large-scale development of low-grade ores in
Montana, and can now supply all of our needs
from this source.

Chromite	Occurs in grains, masses, or iso-
$FeCr_2O_4$	metric octahedrons; hardness 5.5;
chromic iron	specific gravity 4.4; color black;

streak dark-brown; luster submetallic; opaque
on thin edges.

In form, color and streak chromite resembles
magnetite and franklinite. From the magnetite
it is distinguished by being non-magnetic; from
the franklinite, by being insoluble in hydrochloric acid, while the franklinite is soluble.
Chromite furnishes practically all the chromium
used in the arts and manufactures. It is a
mineral associated with high temperatures, and
therefore found in dark lavas, serpentine, and
olivine. It occurs in Pennsylvania, Maryland,
New Jersey, Montana, Oregon, Wyoming, and
California.

TUNGSTEN

This element is obtained either as a heavy
dark-gray metal, which is very hard and difficult

to fuse, or as a dark-gray powder. It is used as an alloy with iron, one part of tungsten to nine of steel, to make the ferrotungsten, which has extraordinary hardness, and is used mostly for high-speed tools. Tungsten is also one of the three metals (cobalt, chromium and tungsten) which are alloyed together to make stellite. Some of the tungsten supply is also used to make the films in incandescent lamps, and in some of the chemical industries. It has but one important ore, wolframite, and this is found in the United States in but small quantities; so that we ordinarily have to import the greater part of what we use. During the last war, under the stimulus of high prices and the urge of necessity, we did find and produce substantial quantities of tungsten. China is the world's largest producer of tungsten ore with Burma second, and the United States a poor third.

Wolframite (FeMn) WO₄ Occurs in monoclinic crystals or in crystalline masses; hardness 5.5; specific gravity 7.4; color dark-brown to black; streak nearly black; lustre submetallic; opaque on thin edges.

If in crystals the form will serve to distinguish this mineral from cassiterite and ilmenite, the two which it most resembles; but if it is massive the only sure way to decide is to put a piece in strong sulphuric acid; if it dissolves and throws down a yellow precipitate (tungstic acid) it is wolframite.

Like the two other minerals mentioned above it occurs in veins in igneous rocks, being associated with high temperatures. As it is almost insoluble in water, like cassiterite and ilmenite, it is likely to occur with them in the sands which are the result of the disintegration of the rocks which carried the minerals; and so a large part of the supply today comes from placer deposits.

It is found in Connecticut, North Carolina, Missouri, Colorado, and California.

RADIUM, URANIUM AND VANADIUM

These three metals are all rare and occur together. Radium, discovered in 1898, is a heavy metal which has proved very useful because of its radio-activity, that is, its power of giving off or radiating tiny particles of matter known as *X-rays*, part of which are charged with positive electricity, and part of them with negative electricity. The ability of these rays to pass through other substances has made possible photographing the denser substances within those less dense, as the bones within the flesh, or metal within leather or wood, etc. The rays have proved of great value medicinally, and are also used to make objects luminous in the dark. These X-rays are also used in the study of the ultimate structure of matter, as it can be thus obtained in such small units.

Uranium is another element which is radioactive and can be used for many of the same purposes as radium.

Vanadium, the third of these associated metals,

and the commonest of the group, is not radio-active. It is a silvery-white metal, mostly used as an alloy with steel to give it great hardness.

Carnotite
Pl. 27
$K_2O \cdot 2U_2O_3 \cdot$
$V_2O_5 \cdot 3H_2O$

Occurs in earthy masses; color yellow.

This mineral is included here, not because it is common, but because it is of such great interest. It is the chief source of supply in the United States of radium, uranium and vanadium. It is a lemon-yellow earth or powder, which looks a little like orpiment. It is however found in a sandstone, instead of where hot waters have deposed minerals. From a ton of this ore about 10 pounds of uranium oxide, 55 pounds of vanadium and $\frac{1}{1000}$th of a gram of radium are obtained. Carnotite is found in south-west Colorado and south-east Utah, and on Carrizo Mountain on the line between Arizona and New Mexico.

MERCURY

Mercury, or quicksilver, is the only metal which is liquid at ordinary temperatures. It is silvery-white in color, with a striking metallic luster, and at the low temperature of 662° F., boils and changes to a colorless vapor. Mercury alloys with certain metals, these alloys being known as amalgams. In this way it is especially useful for the recovery of gold and silver, the mercury being added to crushed ore, the gold or silver uniting with the mercury in a liquid amalgam, which is then drawn off and heated to a temperature above 662° F., at which temperature the mercury volatilizes and is recovered, while the gold or silver remains behind. Mercury also forms a solid amalgam with tin which is used to coat glass, the high metallic luster making the most effective looking glass. It is also used in medicines (calomel, corrosive sublimate, etc.), for scientific instruments (thermometers, barometers, etc.), in cosmetics, in paints for ship bottoms, etc.

Though there are some 25 minerals of mercury, only one is common or important as a source of the metal, cinnabar. The United States is self-sufficient as far as mercury is concerned, producing just about as much as it uses. The leading producers are Spain, Austria, Italy, and the United States. Commercially mercury is quoted as quicksilver, and in flasks of 75 pounds each.

Cinnabar
HgS, Pl. 27
Occurs in massive or earthy form, or in minute crystals in cavities; hardness 2.5; specific gravity 8; color scarlet to dark red; streak vermilion; luster adamantine; translucent on thin edges.

The bright-red color and the streak are usually enough to identify this mineral at once, but some of the darker varieties resemble hematite or zincite in appearance, but both these have much greater hardness. When in crystals they are tiny hexagonal prisms with pyramids on the end. Cinnabar is usually found in or near metamorphic or igneous rocks, either in veins leading from the igneous rocks, or in metamorphic rocks, or it may occur disseminated through metamorphic rocks. It is associated with quartz or calcite, and may occur with other sulphides like pyrite, galena, argentite, etc. It is most abundant in California, but is also found in Oregon, Washington, Idaho, Arizona, Nevada, Utah, Texas, and Montana.

TIN

Tin has been known since early Roman times, and the mines at Cornwall, England, were worked from that time all through down to the present, but now they are becoming of minor importance as they approach exhaustion. The metal is silvery-white, does not easily tarnish, is malleable, but has little ductility and little tensile strength. Tin is mostly used in making tin plate, a thin sheet of steel covered with tin, the tin being only 1 to 2% of the total weight. This tin plate is mostly made into tin cans, and used as containers for food. Some tin is used in making solder, tin-foil, tubes for paste, vaseline, etc., and around 1000 tons per year for weighting silk. This "weighting" makes the silk heavier by about 25% and gives it a "rustle," which, while much in evidence, is really indicative that the silk is not pure. The United States produces very little tin, most of the world's supply coming from the Malay Peninsula, Dutch East Indies, China, and Bolivia, with small amounts from several other countries.

Cassiterite
SnO_2, Pl. 28
tin stone
Occurs in tetragonal crystals, massive, or in grains and pebbles; hardness 6.5; specific gravity 7; color black or dark-brown; streak gray; luster adamantine; translucent on thin edges.

The crystals are short prisms with pyramidal ends. Twinning is common. Cassiterite also occurs in fibrous masses, and when it is weathered from its original location, is so insoluble and hard, that it remains as grains and pebbles, making placer-deposits, from which today three quarters of the supply is obtained. If pure, the crystals would be colorless, but impurities of iron and titanium give it the dark-brown to black color. Cassiterite may appear very like rutile, the crystalline forms being identical, but the reddish tinge of color in the rutile will separate the two.

Cassiterite is one of those minerals which result from deposition at very high temperatures, probably from vapors, and is found in the veins in igneous rocks, such as light-colored granites, gneisses, syenites, etc. While not mined in this country it is found in small quantities in Maine, Massachusetts, New Hampshire, Virginia, Alabama, Wyoming, Montana, and California.

TITANIUM

Titanium, as a metal, is a heavy, gray, iron-like powder, which is chiefly useful as an alloy with iron, giving it toughness, and preventing bubbles and cracks in casting. It is not as rare as some other metals which have found a wider use.

Rutile
TiO_2, Pl. 28

Occurs in tetragonal crystals, and in grains; hardness 6.5; specific gravity 4.2; color red to reddish-brown; streak yellowish-brown; luster metallic to adamantine; translucent on thin edges.

Rutile usually occurs in crystals, which are either short and stout, or in needle-like crystals. Twinning is common. In form and general appearance it resembles cassiterite, but the reddish color, and the yellowish-brown streak will distinguish the rutile. It is found in similar rocks, granites, gneisses, syenites, and mica-schists, the two minerals cassiterite and rutile often occurring together. This is also true of the grains, which have been weathered out and are found in sands and gravels of placer deposits. It is found in small quantities in all the New England States, New York, and all down the Appalachian Mountains, especially at Graves Mountain, Ga., and in Arkansas and Alaska.

Ilmenite
$FeTiO_3$

Occurs in granular masses, as black sand, or as tabular hexagonal crystals; hardness 5–6; specific gravity 4.7; color black; streak brownish-red to black; luster metallic; opaque on thin edges.

When ilmenite occurs in crystals they are tabular and resemble hematite in its darker varieties, but the streak readily distinguishes the two. In masses it looks like magnetite, but the lack of magnetism serves to distinguish these two minerals. It is very likely to be associated with cassiterite, rutile, or magnetite in grains which have weathered out of the original rock, and have resisted solution and wear. Sands with a large amount of the above mentioned minerals are termed "black sands," some of which are important for one or another of these minerals.

Ilmenite is a mineral formed at high temperatures, and probably often deposited from hot vapors. It is found in granites, syenites, and gneisses. Among the better known localities are Orange, N. Y., Litchfield, Conn., Florida, California, etc.

PLATINUM

This metal is steel-gray in color, very malleable and ductile, almost infusible and resists the action of acids. It is one of the "noble" metals, much rarer than gold, and so has become popular for jewelry. It is also used in the manufacture of sulphuric-acid, in nitrogen-fixation plants, for chemical utensils, in the electrical industries, and in dentistry. Platinum in its occurrence is associated with the certain other equally rare elements, like iridium, palladium and osmium. Its use has increased rapidly of late, but the supply has not kept up with the demand, so that, whereas in 1906 platinum and gold were about equally valuable, now the platinum brings about five times as much as the gold.

Platinum Pt. Occurs in grains or nuggets; hardness 4.5; specific gravity 19 (21 if pure); color steel-gray: luster metallic; opaque.

This rare metal is mostly found in placer-deposits, often with gold. It comes originally from dark igneous rocks, like peridotite, pyroxenite, etc., and platinum is found to be associated with the nickel ores of Sudbury, Canada. While formerly 90% of the world's supply of platinum came from placer mines in the Ural Mountains, today more than half is produced in Canada and about a fifth in Russia. In the United States it is found in California, Oregon, Nevada, and Alaska.

THE MAGNESIUM GROUP

Magnesium is a silvery-white metal, easily tarnished by exposure to moist air. Because of its light weight, less than twice the weight of water, and strength, it is being substituted for aluminum, especially in airplanes, where the question of weight is crucial. It is also used in automobile and ship production and other machine industries, and in the manufacture of flares and incendiary bombs. Magnesium is obtained chiefly from magnesite, dolomite, and in the United States as a result of a recently developed process, from sea water. Magnesium has a considerable number of minerals, of which three are taken up here and several more under the head of silicates, where both magnesium and silicon are combined in a mineral.

Spinel $MgAlO_4$. Pl. 29

Occurs mostly as isometric octahedrons; hardness 8; specific gravity 3.5; color, red, yellow, green, or black; streak white; luster vitreous; transparent on thin edges.

This is a rather rare mineral, but, when in clear crystals is considered one of the gems. It was early confused with corundum, and the red variety called ruby, as it was found in the same gem-bearing sands in Ceylon, Burma, and Siam. However the form of the isometric octahedron as compared with the hexagonal prism of the corundum, together with the lesser hardness are sufficient to distinguish the two easily. The crystals are usually octahedrons, but may have the corners cut or the edges beveled. Twins are not uncommon.

The standard color is a clear deep-red, and such a spinel is known in the gem trade as a *spinel-ruby*. If the color is rose-red, it is a *Balas ruby;* if orange, it is *rubicelle*, if of a violet tinge, *almandine*. When small quantities of other elements replace the magnesium, the color is greatly changed. For example a little iron present gives the crystals a dark-green to black color, and the spinel is known as *ceylonite*. If there is both iron and chromium present, the color becomes yellowish or greenish-brown, and this variety is *picotite*. When the impurities are iron and copper, the color becomes grass-green, and it is called *chlorospinel*. A form, in which the magnesium is completely replaced by iron, is black in color and termed *hercynite*, and occurs fairly abundantly in Westchester Co., N. Y. From Amity, N. Y., to Andover, N. J., there is a belt of granular limestone in which spinel of all colors is found. St. Lawrence Co., N. Y., is also a rich locality. Bolton, Mass., Newton, Sterling, and Sparta, N. J., North Carolina, Alabama, and California all yield spinel.

Magnesite
$MgCO_3$.
Occurs in cleavable or compact porcelain-like masses; hardness 4; specific gravity 3.1: color white to gray: luster vitreous; translucent on thin edges.

Magnesite is white and brittle, and cleaves perfectly parallel to the faces of the rhombohedron, but it seldom occurs in crystals. It will effervesce in warm hydrochloric acid and has some resemblance to calcite, but can be distinguished by the greater hardness. It is still more like dolomite, both having the same color and cleavage, both effervescing in warm hydrochloric acid; but the magnesite has half a point greater hardness and the porcelainous appearance. Magnesite is used in toilet preparations, paper making, and mixed with asbestos, as a covering for heating pipes.

Magnesite is found in Massachusetts, Pennsylvania, Texas, and in large deposits in California and Washington.

Dolomite Occurs in crystals, or in cleavable
(MgCa)CO₃ or granular masses; hardness 3.5;
Pl. 29 & 19 specific gravity 2.8; color white to
pink or gray; streak white; luster vitreous;
transparent on thin edges.

Dolomite crystallizes in the hexagonal system,
in rhombohedrons (hemihedral form), which are
more or less modified by faces on the corners or
edges. The cleavage is parallel to the rhombohedron, and it will effervesce in warm hydrochloric acid. Sometimes the crystal faces are
curved, and when this is the case, dolomite is
easily determined. Usually however dolomite
resembles both calcite and magnesite. From the
calcite it is distinguished by the greater hardness,
and from magnesite by lesser hardness and not
being porcelainous in appearance. Some of the
commoner forms are shown on Plate 29, crystals
like C being found embedded in anhydrite and
gypsum.

Magnesium is a common element and is likely
to be present wherever lime is being deposited,
so dolomite crystals are common, and much of
the limestone is dolomitic.

It may be found in almost any limestone
section of the country. Some of the finest
crystals of dolomite however come from Rox-
bury, Vt., Smithfield, R. I., Hoboken, N. J.,
Lockport, Rochester, and Niagara Falls, N. Y.,
etc.

SILICON, SILICA AND THE SILICATES

Silicon is one of the non-metallic elements, and
does not occur as such in Nature. When isolated

It is either a dark-brown powder, or steel-gray crystals. However silicon is next to oxygen in its importance in making the crust of the earth. Forty-seven per cent of the surface rocks are composed of oxygen, and 28% of silicon, the latter appearing in a host of minerals. The oxide of silicon is termed silica (SiO_2), its crystal form being quartz, the commonest of all minerals. In non-crystalline form silica is also widely distributed, as chalcedony and opal, even appearing in the tissues of animals and plants, as in the feathers of birds, the shells of certain Protozoa (Radiolaria), the spicules of sponges; and in plants, as the shells of diatoms, and in the stalks of grasses, especially cereals and bamboo. Silica in the form of sand is widely used in making glass, porcelain, china, etc., and in the various cements.

Then there are a considerable number of acids of silicon, which do not occur in Nature, but their salts do, and make a host of minerals, which are known as the silicates, such as mica, feldspar, hornblende, etc. Either as quartz, or as silicates, silicon is represented in most all the igneous and metamorphic rocks and in many of the sedimentary rocks.

Quartz
SiO_2, Pl. 30

Occurs as hexagonal crystals, or in grains or masses; hardness 7; specific gravity 2.65; colorless when pure; luster vitreous; transparent on thin edges.

Quartz is not hard to identify. Its hardness and the crystal-form separate it from most all other minerals. It is the most common mineral, making 12% of the earth's crust. The usual crystal form is a hexagonal prism with the sides horizontally striated, and a six-sided pyramid on one or both ends. This six-sided pyramid is really two rhombohedrons, a right-handed one and a left-handed one, so that the alternate faces of the pyramid may show peculiarities, for instance three may be large and three small, as in Fig. B, Plate 30, or the alternate ones may be duller or etched in some manner. The crystals are clear and when pure colorless, but there is a tendency for some slight impurity to color them almost any hue.

The most perfect double-ended crystals form only where growth is possible in all directions, as in clay. In cavities and caves there is an opportunity for the crystals to grow in toward the open spaces, and in such places, one finds fine large crystals; the Alps, Brazil, Japan, and Madagascar being especially famous localities. The largest quartz crystal on record is one 25 feet in circumference which came from Madagascar. In this country the caves at Little Rock, Ark., have furnished some very fine large crystals. Smaller, but very clear crystals, come from about Herkimer, N. Y. Some of these have been used as "Rhine-stones" and as cheap imitations of diamonds. Clear quartz is beautiful enough to be a gem, but it is too common to interest people as jewelry, however many objects of art have been carved from it. One of these took the form of crystal balls, which, through the Middle Ages particularly, developed into a form of mysticism. The gazing into the crystal ball was supposed to give some people supernatural vision. It seems to be a form of hypnotism, gazing at the bright reflecting surface tiring the eye, and making possible visions, which are subjective rather than anything external.

Silica is slightly soluble in water, especially when it is alkaline; so that most river-,lake-, and sea-waters have some silica in solution, and are carrying it from one place to another. The waters, which percolate through the rocks, carry even more, and when they come out into open spaces, they give up some of the silica, making crystals lining these openings, whether fissures or cavities. Not infrequently these silica-bearing waters dissolve out some other crystal, and then deposit in its place silica, thus making a crystal which has the form of what was dissolved, rather than that of quartz. Such a form is known as a pseudomorph.

When molten masses of igneous rock were cooling the quartz crystals had their faces interfered with as they grew, and we have resulting crystalline quartz, simply filling in the spaces between the other crystals, such as feldspar and mica, in the granite. Quartz is a large component in many igneous rocks, also in metamorphic rocks, and certain sedimentary rocks like sandstone are almost wholly made up of quartz grains. Quartz is also the gangue mineral in many veins. In this case it seems to have been deposited from hot water or vapors, as they rose from cooling magmas. With it are associated all sorts of metallic ores as has been suggested.

Quartz has been largely used to make imitations of other much rarer minerals, sometimes in its crystalline form to imitate the diamond, at other times ground and made into a "paste," which is colored to imitate other gems. This paste is a mixture of about 4 parts of quartz, 5 parts of red lead and 1 part of potassium carbonate, melted and cooled slowly. It is clear and has a brilliant luster like the diamond. If some coloring matter is put into it it can be used for rubies, sapphires, etc. When there is any reason to think that this is being used, it is easily detected by being so much softer than any of the true gems, and even than true quartz. Quartz will scratch glass readily, but this imitation has only the hardness of very soft glass, or about 5.

Varieties of Quartz

Rock crystal is the term applied to quartz when it is clear and colorless.

Milky quartz is the milky variety, the whiteness being due to imperfections in the crystallization, such as cracks, bubbles, etc.

Smoky quartz is the cloudy brown-colored variety, which results from the presence of small quantities of organic matter (hydrocarbons) in the quartz. If the color is so dark as to be almost black it is termed **morion.** In the above cases the color will disappear if the stone is heated. Pebbles of smoky quartz from Cairngorm, Scotland, have been so widely used as semiprecious stones that they have come to be known as **cairngorms.**

Citrine, or **false topaz,** is a clear yellow variety, the color again due to the presence of organic matter. It is distinguished from true topaz by the lesser hardness, this having the hardness of 7, while true topaz has a hardness of 8.

Amethyst is quartz with a violet color, due to the presence of small quantities of manganese. To be suitable for cutting into gems, the color must be deep or the small pieces will appear almost colorless. It is widely used today as a semiprecious stone in jewelry; and in the fifteenth century it had the traditional virtue of making the wearer sober-minded, whether he had taken too freely of wine, or was over excited by love-passion.

Rose quartz gets its pale-red color from the presence of a small amount of titanium. It is widely distributed, but is more abundant in the Black Hills of South Dakota.

Aventurine is quartz which has inclosed tiny scales of mica or hematite giving it a spangled appearance.

Prase is a green quartz, the color being due to the inclusion of fibrous crystals of green actinolite.

Cat's Eye is a quartz which has inclosed silky fibers of asbestos. When this is cut parallel to the fibers, the effect is opalescent. The colors are greenish, yellowish-gray, and brown. This form, however, is not to be confused with the true or Oriental Cat's Eye, which is chrysoberyl and has the hardness of 8.

Chalcedony SiO_2 Non-crystalline, occurring in botryoidal, stalactitic or concretionary masses; hardness, 7; specific gravity, 2.65; color white when pure; luster waxy; translucent to transparent on thin edges.

In addition to the crystalline form, silica is freely deposited in an amorphous or cryptocrystalline form which has the same properties as quartz, except the crystal faces. This is called chalcedony, and it occurs in seams, cavities and free surfaces. When the surface of a chalcedony deposit is free it has a waxy luster. It is generally very brittle and breaks in a peculiar splintery manner. Like quartz it also has a great many varieties, according to the impurities present. Its wide distribution, hardness, and the manner in which it can be chipped have made this a most important stone in the history of the development of civilization. The early men first broke it into rough tools, such as knives, axes, spear points, etc., and used these as cutting tools, of one sort or another, because they held their edge better than most stones. We apply, to the people who used only these chipped stones as tools, the term "*Men of the Old Stone Age*," or the period is termed the *Palæolithic Age*. Later men learned how to grind the edge to a smoother outline, and this much shorter period is termed the *Neolithic Age*. The use of flints for the first tools is world-wide, and the American Indian when discovered was still using chalcedony in its rough-hewn state.

"There the ancient Arrow-maker
Made his arrow heads of sandstone,
Arrow heads of chalcedony,
Arrow heads of flint and jasper,
Smoothed and sharpened at the edges,
Hard and polished, keen and costly."

Chalcedony is the proper term to use when the color is white to translucent, in which case the surfaces are usually botryoidal and waxy.

Carnelian is chalcedony which is clear red in color and translucent. This is one of the first stones used for ornamental purposes and for engraving. Carnelians with figures engraved on them were used by the Egyptians, Assyrians and The Children of Israel, at least 2000 B.C.; and the Egyptian scarabs of the fifth or sixth century B.C., were often carved from this variety of chalcedony, as well as from jasper and agates.

The brownish varieties are termed *sard*.

Chrysoprase is an apple-green variety of chalcedony the color being due to the presence of nickel oxide. This is by no means as common as most of the varieties of chalcedony, and was long prized as a gem.

Plasma is chalcedony with a leek- to emerald-green color, and the same stone when it has small red spots of jasper in it is termed *blood-stone*, or *heliotrope*. These red spots are said by tradition to be drops of the blood of Christ.

Jasper is a deep red chalcedony, the color being due to hematite, which is so abundant as to make it opaque. A brown variety colored by limonite is also called jasper, and even green jaspers are found. In all cases the opaque character is common.

Flint is an impure brown chalcedony, usually forming concretions. The color is due to organic matter. Flint is mostly found in limestone or chalk, and the concretions are the result of the small particles of silica scattered through the rock being dissolved, and then reprecipitated about some organic center. Generally the silica was obtained by the dissolution of small fossils, like the shells of diatoms or sponge spicules.

Hornstone and **Chert** are simply impure varieties of flint, brown in color, and with a splintery fracture.

Agate, Plate 32, is a banded or cloudy chalcedony which has formed in a cavity, the layers of different color representing deposition from water, carrying first silica with one impurity, then later, silica with another impurity. Gradually the cavity has been thus filled with silica; and when the mass is freed by the weathering away of the surrounding rock, these banded masses are found. Sometimes the manner of deposition has changed, and while the outer part of the cavity was filled with chalcedony, the central part will contain quartz crystals. On account of the beauty of the colors, and the unusual way in which they may be developed, agates are widely used for semiprecious jewelry and objects of art, and this has been true since ancient times, the name itself coming from the River Achates in Sicily. The center for cutting and polishing agates is at Oberstein, Germany, where this work has been carried on since the middle of the fifteenth century. In spite of the many fine natural colors in agates, they are sometimes artificially colored, in many cases by meththods which are kept as "trade secrets." The color seldom penetrates far; so that even slight chipping reveals whether an inferior agate has been taken and colored up, or whether the stone is natural. Moss agates are chalcedony which has inclosed dendritic masses of some one of the manganese compounds as shown under manganite, p. 73.

Onyx is a variety of agate where the bands are alternately black and white; while **sardonyx** is agate with red or brown bands alternating with the white. Such agates as these are especially desirable for cameo work, where the figure is carved in the chalcedony of one color, and the other color makes the background.

Silicified or **agatized wood** is a form of chalcedony, where silica has replaced wood, molecule by molecule; so that in good specimens, all the structure of the wood is still retained, and when thin sections are made it can be studied under the microscope almost as well as modern wood. This takes place under water, usually, if not always, in fresh water. Such fossilized wood is widely distributed in the western United States, the most famous cases being the Fossil Forest of Arizona, now a National Reservation, and the fossil trees in the Yellowstone National Park.

Opal   Non-crystalline, massive, stalac-
$SiO_2 . H_2O$ titic or nodular; hardness, 6; speci-
Pl. 33   fic gravity 2; all colors; luster vitreous, resinous, or pearly; transparent on thin edges.

Opal differs from chalcedony in having water, usually about 10%, incorporated in its structure. This is water of crystallization, and not firmly held; so that, if opal is heated in a closed tube to above 100 C., it is given off as a vapor. Opal is distinguished from chalcedony by its lesser hardness, and the resinous to pearly luster. It forms in cavities, in layers often of extreme thinness.

Opal is originally the product of the dissolution of silicate minerals in hot acid waters, the resulting gelatinous silica, when it is deposited and hardened, becoming the opal. There are many varieties, some of them highly prized as gems in spite of the moderate hardness and opacity of the mineral. Gem-quality opal gets its opalescent character from the successive deposition of thin films of opal, the light penetrating and being reflected from different films. This breaks up the white light and causes the play of colors which is the charm of this gem.

Precious opal, in which the play of colors is finest, comes mostly from Hungary, Mexico, and Queensland. The opal was a favorite stone from before Roman times, and in its early history was a charm against the "evil eye." During the nineteenth century for some reason it came to be considered an unlucky stone.

Fire opal is a hyacinth-red to honey-yellow variety, which has a fire-like play of color, and is found in Mexico and Honduras.

Common opal does not have the play of color, but comes in a variety of colors; is waxy or greasy in luster; and occurs mostly as fillings of seams or cavities, especially those in igneous rocks, like the steam holes in lavas, etc. It is found in Cornwall, Penn., in Colorado, California, etc.

Opal-agate is a variety in which there are color bands, and it is widely distributed.

Opalized wood is formed in exactly the same

manner as agatized wood, much of the fossil wood called silicified being really opalized.

Siliceous sinter is the porous mass of opal which is so frequently deposited about hot springs and geysers. It is readily recognized by its porous character.

The shells of the diatoms, which are microscopic plants, are made of opal; and while they are so small, there is certainly no other plant so abundant or omnipresent, living as it does in every pool, lake, or sea by the millions. These shells are very indestructible so that they accumulate at the bottom of ponds, bogs, and sea-bottoms, making at times extensive deposits. This material in quantities is termed diatomaceous earth, or **tripolite** (from Tripoli where it was first used commercially). It is used as a polishing powder for metals, marble, glasses, etc.

The Feldspars

The term feldspar is a family name for a large variety of very common minerals, which altogether make up nearly 60% of the crust of the earth, being the predominant part of granites, gneisses, and lavas. In composition they are silicates of aluminum, together with potassium, sodium and calcium, and their mixtures. They may be tabulated as follows:

1. $KAlSi_3O_8$, *orthoclase*, the silicate of aluminum and potassium.

2. $NaAlSi_3O_8$, *albite*, the silicate of aluminum and sodium.

3. $CaAlSi_2O_8$, *anorthite*, the silicate of aluminum and calcium.

4. Mixtures of 1 and 2 are *alkalic feldspar*.
5. Mixtures of 2 and 3 are *plagioclase feldspar*.

Orthoclase is monoclinic, but the rest of the feldspars are triclinic. If crystals are available they may be short and stout, or tabular and thin, but as the feldspars are mostly components of the igneous rocks, where perfect crystals have not had a chance to grow, they are mostly determined by their hardness and cleavage. The hardness of all the feldspars is 6 or very close to it.

They all have three planes of cleavage, two of which are good and intersect either at 90° as in orthoclase, or at about 86° as in the plagioclase series; while the third cleavage plane is imperfect. In figure 1, Plate 34, a and b are the two perfect cleavages, while c is the imperfect one. Breaking into such cleavage masses as the one illustrated is characteristic of feldspar. The specific gravity ranges from 2.55 to 2.75. The luster is vitreous, and the color white, ranging to various shades of gray and pink, and, sometimes in recent lavas, colorless.

Twinning is very common and helps to distinguish orthoclase from the plagioclase feldspars. In orthoclase the twins are simple, that is, only two crystals growing together, and are united on one of the faces, as if one of them had been revolved 180° with the other; or, while related to each other as in the preceding case, they may seem to grow through each other. On plate 34 are three orthoclase crystals showing this simple type of twinning. The first (A) is a simple crystal; the second (B) shows the simplest type of twinning where the left-hand crystal has revolved

180° on the p face, and the end is composed, half of the upper end of one crystal, and half of the lower end of the adjacent crystal. The presence of reëntrant angles calls attention to the twinning. The third figure (C) is a case of intergrowing crystals.

In the plagioclase feldspars twinning is multiple, a large number of crystals, each thin, sometimes as thin as paper, growing side by side, the first one in normal position, the next at 180° with it, the third revolved 180° to the second and thus parallel to the first, and so on. The result is first of all a striated appearance, and second that, as plagioclase crystals have their prism faces intersecting at 86°, there is a series of low roofs and valleys, which are best seen by holding the piece of feldspar so the light reflects from a cleavage face, when it will appear striated; then by tilting it about 8 degrees a second set of reflections, also appearing striated, will appear. The light was first reflected from one side of the roofs, and in the second case from the other side. Figure D, Pl. 34, is a diagram showing the relation of the individual crystals in a multiple twinned piece of plagioclase, in which the crystals are represented as rather large. Plate 35, under labradorite, shows a photograph of a cleavage piece, on which is readily seen the striation which is characteristic of the plagioclase feldspars.

Mixtures of albite and anorthite occur in bewildering numbers, one or the other predominating, and each mixture being uniform throughout the crystal and in the whole mass; so each combination is a mineral, each with its special properties; but the different plagioclase feldspars are so similar in appearance, that by the naked eye it is impossible to separate the closely related ones. This can be done under the microscope by studying the angles at which light is cut off, and also by chemical analyses. For our purposes six types will suffice to illustrate the group, and their composition may be indicated as follows.

Albite is albite with up to 15% of anorthite mixed with it.

Oligoclase is albite with from 15–25% of anorthite mixed with it.

Andesite is albite with from 25–50% of anorthite mixed with it.

Labradorite is anorthite with from 25–50% of albite mixed with it.

Bytownite is anorthite with from 15-25% of albite mixed with it.

Anorthite is anorthite with up to 15% of albite mixed with it.

The best method for distinguishing these feldspars of the plagioclase group is to measure the angle between the two perfect cleavage faces, and even this requires careful measurement. The angles between these faces are as follows:

Orthoclase	90°	Andesite	86° 14′
Microcline	89° 30′	Labradorite	86° 14′
Albite	86° 24′	Bytownite	86° 14′
Oligoclase	86° 32′	Anorthite	86° 50′

Orthoclase
$KAlSi_3O_8$
Occurs in granites, syenites, gneisses and light-colored lavas; hardness, 6; specific gravity, 2.57; color white to gray or pink; cleavage in two direc-

tions perfect and at 90°, in the third direction imperfect; luster vitreous; translucent on thin edges.

Orthoclase is monoclinic, and when formed in cavities develops as crystals, but it is usually a constituent of igneous rocks, in which case the crystals have not had the opportunity to develop the crystal faces, and the orthoclase is in grains or irregular masses; and the best way of determining the mineral is the cleavage, the two perfect cleavage planes intersecting at right angles. Twinning is frequent but of the simple type, only two crystals being united, similar to either B or C on plate 34.

It is found in granites, gneisses or lavas, wherever they occur, being especially characteristic of the granites of the Rocky Mountains.

Microcline Occurs in granites and gneisses
$KAlSi_3O_8$ as crystals or irregular masses; hard-
Pl. 35 ness, 6; specific gravity, 2.56; color white to gray, pink, or greenish; luster vitreous; translucent on thin edges.

Microcline has the same composition as orthoclase, but is in the triclinic system, the c axis being inclined a half degree away from a right angle with the b axis. This is best seen in the cleavage pieces, the two perfect cleavage planes meeting at 89° 30′, and this is the only test for determining this mineral by the unaided eye. Pike's Peak is the best known locality for microcline, and there it occurs in fine large crystals of greenish color, which are known as *Amazon stone.*

Albite
$NaAlSi_3O_8$

Occurs in small crystals, or more often in lamellar masses in granites or in seams in metamorphic rocks; hardness, 6; specific gravity, 2.62; color white to gray; luster vitreous.

Albite may occur in simple crystals, in which case the two perfect cleavage planes meet at an angle of 86° 24′. However, it is much more frequently found twinned in the multiple manner, the individual crystals often being as thin as paper. This gives rise to a fine striation on the end of a crystal, or on the surface made by the imperfect cleavage plane. Where the crystals are extremely thin, the surface may have a pearly luster. Albite types of granite often inclose secondary minerals, that are prized as gems, such as topaz, tourmaline, and beryl.

It is found at Paris, Me., Chesterfield, Mass., Acworth, N. H., Essex Co., N. Y., Unionville, Penn., and in Virginia, and throughout the Rocky Mountains.

Oligoclase
(NaCa) $AlSi_3O_8$

Generally found in cleavable masses in granites and lavas, rarely in crystals; hardness, 6; specific gravity, 2.65; color white, greenish or pink; luster vitreous; translucent on thin edges.

Oligoclase is a plagioclase feldspar and is distinguished by its two perfect cleavage planes meeting at an angle of 86° 32′, but otherwise it is very like albite. Crystals are not common, and it occurs mostly in masses, making one of the components of granite or lava.

It is found in St. Lawrence Co., N. Y., Danbury and Haddam, Conn., Chester, Mass., Unionville, Penn., Bakersville, N. C., etc.

Labradorite
(NaCa) AlSi₃O₈
Pl. 35

Usually found in cleavable masses in granites and lavas; hardness, 6; specific gravity 2.71; color, gray or white, often with a play of colors; luster vitreous; translucent on thin edges.

Labradorite is distinguished by having the two perfect cleavage planes meet at 86° 14'. The iridescent play of color is also very characteristic and is generally present. It is due to the inclusion of minute impurities. This feldspar is usually associated with granites or lavas in which the dark minerals predominate. It gets its name from being the feldspar of the granites of Labrador, and is also found in the granites of the central part of the Adirondack Mountains and the Wichita Mountains of Arkansas.

THE PYROXENE GROUP

The minerals of this group are generally associated with feldspars, and make the dark-colored component of granites, gneisses and lavas. This is especially true of those which have some iron in the crystal. Pyroxenes are salts of metasilicic acid ($H_2 SiO_3$), in which the hydrogen (H) has been replaced by calcium, magnesium, iron, etc. The commoner minerals are orthorhombic or monoclinic, and all agree in their crystal habit, being short stout prisms, with the vertical edges so beveled that a cross section is eight-sided. The cleavage is good in two directions, parallel to the beveling faces (m in figure b, Plate 36), and they intersect at an angle of 87°. This is very characteristic, and if one has a crystal broken across, it is easy to see and measure this angle of intersection. These pyroxenes have the same chemical composition as the corresponding series of amphiboles, but the two are distinguished by several features. Pyroxenes are short and stout crystals, while amphiboles are long and either blade- or needle-like; pyroxenes are eight-sided in cross section, while amphiboles are six-sided; in pyroxenes the cleavage planes intersect at 87°, while in amphiboles they intersect at 55°. The minerals of this group are most frequently one of the components of a lava or granite, and are less frequently associated with metamorphic rocks. Three are common; enstatite, hypersthene, and augite.

Enstatite
MgSiO₃
Usually occurs in lamellar or fibrous-lamellar masses in dark lavas; hardness, 5.5; specific gravity, 3.3; color gray, bronze or brown; luster vitreous, translucent on thin edges.

Enstatite rarely occurs in crystals, but when it does they are orthorhombic. Usually it is in irregular masses with the cleavage angles, typical of pyroxene. The color is light, that is gray or brownish, and the streak white or nearly so. In most respects it is similar to hypersthene, which has the same composition, except that a large part of the magnesium is replaced by iron, and there are all sorts of gradations between the two minerals. When some iron takes the place of magnesium, the color darkens to, or towards bronze, until when about a third of the magnesium is so replaced, and the color is fully bronze, this variety is called *bronzite*. Bronzite is present in some of the dark lavas like gabbro and peridotite. Enstatite is found in the Adirondack Mountains, at Brewster and Edwards, N. Y., etc.

Hypersthene (MgFe) SiO₃ Occurs in cleavable masses in dark lavas; hardness, 5.5; specific gravity, 3.4; color dark-brown or greenish brown; luster vitreous translucent on thin edges.

Hypersthene is a pyroxene in which magnesium and iron are present in about equal quantities. It is similar to enstatite, except that the color is darker, and the streak gray or brownish gray in color. These two minerals grade into each other, so that there are cases where it is simply a matter of preference as to which name should be given to the mineral. This form is associated with dark lavas, of the gabbro or peridotite type, in such places as the Adirondack Mountains, Mount Shasta in California, Buffalo Peaks, Colo., etc.

Augite CaMg(SiO₃)₂, MgAl SiO₆ + Fe₂O₃ Pl. 36 Usually occurs in short stout monoclinic crystals; hardness, 5.5; specific gravity, 3.3; color dark-green to black; luster vitreous; translucent on thin edges.

Augite is a complex pyroxene having some iron and aluminum always present in it, but the amount not a fixed quantity. It is by far the commonest of the pyroxenes and has a wide distribution, both in the sorts of lavas in which it appears, and in the world. It is commonly the dark component of such lavas, as gabbros and peridotites, and also is common in metamorphic rocks, especially impure crystalline limestones. It is found at Raymond and Mumford, Me., Thetford, Vt., Canaan, Conn., in Weschester, Orange, Lewis and St. Lawrence Counties of N. Y., in Chester Co., Penn., at Ducktown, Tenn., Templeton, Canada, etc.

THE AMPHIBOLE GROUP

The amphiboles are a group of minerals made up of the same chemical elements as the pyroxenes, but with the molecular arrangement different, which appears in the forms of the crystals. The commoner ones are all monoclinic but contrast with the pyroxenes as follows. Amphiboles are long and slender crystals, while pyroxenes are short and stout; amphiboles are six-sided, while pyroxenes are eight-sided; amphiboles have the two perfect cleavages intersecting at 55° and 125°, while those of pyroxene intersect at 87° and 93°. With the above in mind it is easy to place the minerals in their proper group, but inside the group it is not always so easy to distinguish one from another. This group is associated rather with metamorphic rocks than with igneous rocks, with which the pyroxenes are mostly associated. The three commoner minerals of the group are tremolite, actinolite, and hornblende.

Tremolite
$(CaMg)_3 (SiO_3)_4$
Pl. 37
Occurs in long prismatic crystals or in columnar or fibrous masses; hardness 5.5; specific gravity, 3; color white to gray; luster vitreous; transparent on thin edges.

The long prismatic crystals of tremolite occur especially where dolomitic limestones have been altered by metamorphism. Sometimes these crystals grow side by side, making fibrous masses, where the long slender crystals can be picked apart with the fingers, and yet are flexible, and tough enough so that they can be felted together. This is termed asbestos, which, because it is infusible and a poor conductor of heat, is much used to make insulators, fire-proof shingles, and all sorts of fireproof materials. The varieties in which the crystals are finer and silky in appearance, like the one illustrated on Plate 38 are termed *amianthus*. There are other minerals, such as actinolite and serpentine, which occur in the same manner, and are also called asbestos, the serpentine variety being just now the most important commercially.

Tremolite is found at Lee, Mass., Canaan, Conn., Bryam, N. J., in Georgia, etc.

Actinolite
$(CaMgFe)_3$
$(SiO_3)_4$
Occurs in radiating crystals, or in fibrous masses; hardness, 5.5; specific gravity 3; color pale- to dark-green; luster vitreous; translucent on thin edges.

Except for its green color, this mineral is very like tremolite. The difference between the two is due to the small amount of iron in the actinolite. It is usually found in schists, and the radiating character of the crystal groups is enough to determine the mineral, if it is already clear that it is one of the amphiboles. Occasionally it occurs with the crystals parallel to each other, making one of the forms of asbestos.

Actinolite is found at Warwick, Edenville, and Amity in Orange Co., N. Y., at Franklin and Newton, N. J., Mineral Hill and Unionville, Penn., Bare Hills, Md., Willis Mt., Va., etc.

Hornblende Occurs in well-defined crystals, in $(CaMgFe)_3(SiO_3)_4$ grains and in masses; hardness, 5.5; $CaMgAl_2(SiO_4)_3$ specific gravity 3.2; color black, Pl. 37 dark-green, or dark-brown; luster vitreous; translucent on thin edges.

In composition hornblende corresponds to augite, but occurs in long slender, six-sided crystals with cleavage planes intersecting at 55°, so that it is a typical amphibole. It occurs in a very wide range of rocks, such as granite, syenite, diabase, and gabbro; and in such metamorphic rocks as schists and gneisses; and sometimes igneous rocks are made up almost entirely of hornblende, when they are known as amphibolites or hornblendite. It is found all through the New England States, down along the Piedmont Plateau, through the Blue Ridge Mountains, and in many of the western mountainous areas.

THE GARNET GROUP

The garnets are a series of double silicates, which occur with surprizingly uniform characters. They are all isometric, and occur either as dodecahedrons, or as the 24-sided figure (the trapezohedron), which is formed by the beveling of the edges of the dodecahedron, and developing these new faces to the exclusion of the dodecahedron faces. Combinations of the dodecahedron and trapezohedron (36 faces) may occur. All the garnets have a hardness of 7 to 7.5, and the specific gravity runs from 3.2 to 4.3, according to the composition. In size they run from as small as a grain of sand up to as large as a boy's marble, and occasionally even to four inches in diameter. The color varies with the composition, from colorless to yellow, red, violet, or green. There is no cleavage, and the luster is always vitreous.

Garnets are usually accessory minerals, found in metamorphic rocks, though they are sometimes also present in granites and lavas. They are always segregations which have taken place in the presence of high temperatures. When clear and perfect several of the garnets are used as gems. On the other hand some of the common garnets occur in such quantities that they are crushed and used as abrasives, for such work as dental polishes, or for leather and wood polishing.

The following is the composition of some of the commoner garnets.

$$Ca_3 \, Al_2 \, (SiO_4)_3 = grossularite$$
$$Mg_3 \, Al_2 \, (SiO_4)_3 = pyrope$$
$$Fe_3 \, Al_2 \, (SiO_4)_3 = almandite$$
$$Mn_3 \, Al_2 \, (SiO_4)_3 = spessartite$$
$$Ca_3 \, Fe_2 \, (SiO_4)_3 = andradite$$
$$Ca_3 \, Cr_2 \, (SiO_4)_3 = uvarovite$$

Grossularite is chiefly found in crystalline limestones, which have resulted either from contact with lavas, or from general metamorphism of impure limestones. These garnets are colorless to white, or more often shades of yellow, orange, pink, green or brown, according to traces of impurity which they may contain. The cinnamon-colored variety from Ceylon is termed *cinnamon stone*, and is a fairly popular gem.

Pyrope is a deep-red color and when perfect is highly prized as a gem. It is found in dark-colored igneous rocks, like lavas, or serpentines. Some of the finest come from South Africa, where they are found in company with the diamond.

Almandite is dark-red to brown in color, the brownish-cast distinguishing it from pyrope. It is one of the garnets known as "common garnet." In some cases it is clear and deep colored enough to be used as a gem, but mostly it is muddy in appearance. The name almandite comes from Alabanda, a city of the ancient district of Caria, Asia Minor, whence garnets were traded to ancient Rome. The finest garnets "Sirian garnets" came from the city of "Sirian" in Lower Burma, and were supposed to have been found near there, but careful investigation shows that no garnets occurred near there, and this town was therefore, even at that early time, a distributing point for garnets, found probably further to the east. The "Sirian" garnet had a violet cast and now the term is used to indicate a type of garnet, rather than a locality.

Spessartite is dark-hyacinth-red, or red with a violet-tinge, and is one of the less-common garnets. It is usually found in granites. The finest garnets of the type come from Amelia Court House, Va., which has yielded some ranging from one up to a hundred carats.

Andradite is another garnet which is termed "common garnet." It is red in color, but with a yellowish-cast which distinguishes it from almandite, but these two are not easy to separate. It is found mostly in metamorphosed limestones. One variety is black in color and called *malanite*. It is found in lavas. The common yellowish-red garnets are found through New England and the Piedmont Plateau.

Uvarovite is a rare garnet of emerald-green color, found in association with chromium ores.

The number of localities for garnets is so great that a list would suggest most of the regions where metamorphic rocks occur, as all over New England, throughout the Piedmont Plateau, the Rock Mountains, etc. Certain fine clear garnets, found in Montana, northeastern Arizona, and northwestern New Mexico are sold under the trade name of "Montana, Arizona or New Mexico rubies." These are of fine quality and are mostly collected by the Indians from the ant hills and scorpion's nests of those regions.

Garnets are among the earliest stones mentioned in ancient languages, as would be expected from the way these hard and beautiful crystals weather out of the much softer metamorphic rocks, like schists. In the past they, with most any other translucent red stone, were included under the name *carbuncle*. This, however, is not the name of any mineral, but refers rather to a mode of cutting, *en cabochon* or with a convex surface.

GLUCINUM

Glucinum is a rare metal, silvery-white in color, malleable, and melting at a fairly low temperature. It is found in the mineral beryl, from which has come the alternative name *beryllium*. The name comes from the sweet taste of its salts. Except for beryl its minerals are rare, and the metal has found but few uses for man.

Beryl
$Gl_3Al_2 (SiO_3)_6$
Pl. 39

Occurs in hexagonal crystals in granites, gneisses and mica schists; hardness, 7.5; specific gravity, 2.7; color usually some tint of green; luster vitreous; transparent on thin edges.

When this mineral occurs in coarse hexagonal prisms, with or without faces on the ends, it is known as beryl; when the crystals are clear and perfect and of a dark-green color, they are of gem value and are termed *emerald;* when of a light-green color, they are *aquamarine;* and when bright-yellow in color, they are the *golden beryl*. There is little difficulty in determining beryl, for only apatite occurs in such crystals, and is green, and this latter mineral has a hardness of only 5. There is an imperfect basal cleavage.

Ordinary beryl is fairly common in granites of the pegmatite sort, and less common in gneisses and mica-schists. This type often furnishes crystals of large size, up to two and three feet in diameter.

Beryl which is free from cracks and inclosures, so it can be used as a gem, is so rare, that the emerald has a value above that of the diamond, and second only to the ruby. It is one of the gems with a long history, having been quarried on the west coast of the Red Sea at least 1650 B.C. by the Egyptians. To early people it had a power to quicken the prophet instinct and made the wearer see more clearly. The Spanish conquistadores found fine emeralds among the treasures of both Mexico and Peru. In the United States, Stony Point, N. C., was a notable locality for these gems, but now seems to have been exhausted. The name emerald has been applied to many other green stones, usually with some geographical modification, as "Oriental emerald" which is green corundum, "Brazilian emerald" which is tourmaline, etc.

Giant beryls have been found at Acworth and Grafton, N. H., and at Royalston, Mass. Localities for ordinary beryl are Albany, Norway, Bethel, Hebron, Paris, and Topsam, Me., Barre, Goshen and Chesterfield, Mass., New Milford and Branchville, Conn., Chester and Mineral Hill, Penn., Stony Point, N. C., and many other localities in the Appalachians; also Mount Atero, Colo., and in the Black Hills of South Dakota.

Sodalite
$Na_4Al_3Cl(SiO_4)_3$ Occurs in irregular masses, sometimes in dodecahedrons; hardness, 3.5–6; specific gravity, 2.3; color deep-blue to colorless; streak white; luster vitreous; translucent on thin edges.

This striking mineral, with its deep-blue to azure color, is not easily confused with any other. It is characteristic of soda-rich igneous rocks such as syenite and some lavas. In this country it is found at Litchfield, Me., and Salem, Mass.

Zircon   Usually occurs in tetrahedral crys-
ZrSiO₄   tals in igneous rocks; hardness, 7.5;
Pl. 39   specific gravity, 4.7; color brown; luster vitreous; translucent on thin edges.

Zircon, the mineral of the rare earth element zirconium, nearly always occurs in light-colored igneous rocks, like syenite. It may occur in schists or gneisses, but in these rocks the crystals are of microscopic size. Because of their great hardness and insolubility, zircon crystals resist weathering and are often found, along with gold, cassiterite, or magnetite, in sands which have resulted from the disintegration of syenite rocks.

Zircon refracts and disperses light to a degree second only to the diamond, so that clear crystals are sought as gems. They are often called "Matura diamonds" because of their abundance at Matura, Ceylon. When the crystals are colorless or smoky they are termed *jargons* or *jargoons;* when of a red-orange hue, they are *hyacinth* or *jacinth*. Most of the zircon of gem-quality comes from Ceylon, where it is picked up as rolled-pebbles from the beds of brooks.

The most remarkable American locality for zircon is near Green River, in Henderson Co., N. C., where it is found abundantly in a decomposed pegmatite dike, from which many tons have been obtained. It is also found at Moriah.

Warwick, Amity and Diana, N. Y., at Franklin Furnace, and Trenton, N. J., in the gold-bearing sands of California, etc.

Cyanite
Al_2SiO_5
Pl. 40

Occurs in long blade-like crystals in gneisses and schists; hardness, 7 at right angles to the length, and 4.5 parallel to the length; specific gravity 3.6; color blue; luster vitreous; translucent on thin edges.

There are only a few blue minerals, and the way in which cyanite occurs in long thin blade-like crystals is entirely characteristic. If more is still wanted to determine this mineral, its unique character in having the great hardness 7 when scratched parallel to the length, and only 4.5 when scratched crossways, will settle any doubts.

The mineral *sillimanite* has the same composition as cyanite, but is fibrous in habit and has the hardness 6.5. If cyanite is heated to 1350° C. it changes its character and becomes sillimanite.

Cyanite is found as an accessory mineral in metamorphic rocks, such as gneiss and schist, at Chesterfield, Mass., Litchfield and Oxford, Conn., in Chester Co., Penn., in North Carolina, etc.

THE MICA GROUP

The micas are very common minerals, easily recognized by their very perfect basal cleavage, as a result of which thin sheets, often less than a thousandth of an inch in thickness, readily split off. These are tough and elastic, which distinguishes mica from the chlorite group in which there is similar basal cleavage, but the sheets are not elastic.

Micas are complex silicates of aluminum, with potassium, iron, lithium, magnesium and hydrogen. They are one of the principle components of many granites, gneisses, and schists. This mineral is always crystalline, being in the monoclinic system, but occurring in six-sided prisms. The cleavage is so dominant a character that the crystal form is usually overlooked, as it is seldom requisite in determining this mineral. The size of the sheets of mica depend on the size of the crystals, the larger sheets expressing great slowness in cooling from the original magmas. Sometimes the crystals may be two or even three feet in diameter. The hardness is not great, ranging between 2 and 3. The specific gravity lies between 2.7 and 3.2. The color varies according to the composition, from silvery-white, through gray, pink, and green to black. The luster is vitreous to pearly, sometimes gleaming in the darker-colored varieties. The commoner types of mica are as follows:

Muscovite, $H_2 KAl_3 (SiO_4)_3$ or potash mica.

Lepidolite, $LiK (Al_2 OH \cdot F) Al (SiO_3)_3$ or lithia mica.

Biotite, $(HK)_2 (MgFe)_2 Al_2 (SiO_4)_3$ or iron mica.

Phlogopite, $H_2 KMg_3 Al (SiO_8)_3$ or magnesia mica.

Muscovite is colorless, silvery-white, gray or sometimes pale-green or brown. It gets its name from Moscow where it was early used for window panes, and it is still used for stove and furnace doors, as well as in electric work, for a lubricant, etc.

The best crystals occur in granites, in the coarse varieties of which large crystals may be obtained. It is found also as small scales in gneisses and schists, and when weathered from its original rocks it may be present in sandstones and shales. Muscovite is always in its origin an elementary component of deep-seated igneous rocks, like granite; but is never a component of extruded lavas. *Sericite* is muscovite which has been secondarily produced by the alteration of other minerals into muscovite, as when feldspar, cyanite, topaz, etc., have been modified by the presence of heat and hot vapors, when near lavas that have come in contact with other rocks. Muscovite is very resistant to alteration by weathering, but when it does change, the greater part of it becomes kaolin. It is found at Acworth and Grafton, N. H., in plates, sometimes a yard across at Paris, Me., Chesterfield and Goshen, Mass., Portland and Middletown, Conn., at Warwick, Edenville, etc., N. Y., and all down the Appalachian Mts., also in the Rocky Mts., the Cascade Range, etc.

Lepidolite is pink or lilac in color and occurs in scaly masses, mostly in granites. It does not come in large crystals. Lepidolite is found at Paris and Hebron, Me., Middletown, Conn., Pala, Calif., etc.

Biotite is dark-brown or black mica. Like muscovite it is very common, making one of the chief components of granites, gneisses and schists;

and, unlike muscovite, it may occur in extrusive lavas, like trachyte, andesite, and basalt. It resists weathering much less than muscovite, so that, when the rocks of which it is a component disintegrate, biotite is usually altered to kaolin and other compounds. It is likely to occur in good-sized crystals, especially at Topsam, Me., Moriah, N. Y., Easton, Penn., etc.

Phlogopite is pale-brown, often coppery in color, and is most likely to occur in serpentines, or crystalline limestones or dolomites, often in fine crystals, of good size. While one of the less abundant micas, this is found at Gouverneur, Edwards, and Warwick, N. Y., Newton, N. J., and Burgess, Canada.

Topaz
$Al_2F_2SiO_4$
Pl. 41

Occurs in crystals mostly; hardness, 8; specific gravity, 3.5; colorless to pale-yellow; luster vitreous; transparent on thin edges.

Topaz may be colorless, but is more often some shade of yellow, and at times brown or even blue. Its hardness is characteristic, there being but few minerals as hard, and it is used to represent the hardness 8 in the Moh scale. The crystals are orthorhombic prisms, with the edges of the prism beveled and often striated. The ends of crystals usually terminate with a basal plane, parallel to which there is good cleavage. Between this basal plane and the prism faces there are usually several sets of small faces as indicated on Plate 41.

This mineral, as is also true of most minerals containing fluorine, is one of those which have crystallized out from hot vapors, escaping from igneous magmas. It is associated with such minerals, as tourmaline, beryl, fluorite, and cassiterite, and occurs mostly in cavities or seams, in or near granites.

Ordinary topaz, which means crystals that are imperfect by reason of tiny cracks and impurities is not very rare, but crystals which are perfect and clear in color are considered gems. Most of the gem-topaz is some shade of yellow, but may be brown or blue, never, however pink, as is often seen in jewelry. The "pinking" is artificial, and done by packing yellow or brown topaz in magnesia, asbestos, or lime, and then heating it slowly to red heat, after which it is cooled slowly. If underheated the color is salmon, if overheated all color disappears. Topaz has been a gem for centuries, the earliest records coming from Egypt. The name comes from *topazios*, meaning to seek, because the earliest known locality, from which it was gathered, was a little island of that name in the Red Sea, and this island was often surrounded by fog and hard for those early mariners to find. Here by mandate of the Egyptian kings the inhabitants had to collect topazes, and deliver them to the gem-cutters of Egypt for polishing.

Several yellow stones are called topaz, as the "Oriental topaz" which is corundum and more valuable than topaz itself; and several varieties of yellow quartz, which go under such names as "Saxon," "Scotch," "Spanish," and "smoky" topaz. When topaz occurs colorless as in Siberia, the Ural Mountains, and in the state of Minas

Geraes, Brazil, in all of which places it is found as pebbles in brooks, it goes under the name of "slave's diamonds." Brazil is today the chief source of gem-quality topaz.

Ordinary topaz is found in this country at Trumbull, Conn., Crowder's Mt., N. C., Thomas Mts., Utah, in Colorado, Missouri, and California, etc.

Staurolite
$FeAl_5OH$
$(SiO_6)_2$
Pl. 41

Occurs in orthorhombic crystals; hardness, 7.5; specific gravity, 3.7; color brown; luster resinous; translucent on thin edges.

This mineral occurs about equally abundantly in simple crystals similar to the outline on Plate 41, and in twins which have grown through each other either at 90° or at 60°. The color is either brown or reddish-brown. In all cases it is an accessory mineral, occurring in metamorphic rocks, usually schists, though less frequently in slates and gneisses.

From the seventeenth century on, it has been used as a baptismal stone, and worn as a charm, legends stating that it fell from the heavens. Fine crystals have been found in Patrick County, Va., and there is in this region the legend, that when the fairies heard of the crucifixion of Christ, they wept and their tears falling crystallized in the form of crosses, such as the one shown on Plate 41.

Staurolite is found in the schists of New England as at Windham, Me., or Chesterfield, Mass., and all down the east side of the Appalachian Mountains to Georgia.

Olivine
(MgFe)$_2$SiO$_4$
Peridot or
Chrysolite
Occurs in grains and irregular masses in dark lavas; hardness 6.5 to 7; specific gravity 3.3; color bottle- to olive-green; luster vitreous; translucent on thin edges.

Olivine rarely occurs in crystals, but when it does they belong to the orthorhombic system. The dark-green grains or masses are recognized by the color, considerable hardness and indistinct cleavage. Serpentine may have a similar color, but its hardness is only 4. In hydrochloric acid olivine decomposes to a gelatinous mass.

Olivine is typically one of the constituents of the dark lavas, like basalt, gabbro, or peridotite. It is also a common mineral in meteorites. Olivine, in the presence of water, alters to other minerals, especially serpentine, with great facility.

It occurs fairly widely wherever the dark lavas are present, as in the White Mountains of N. H., in Loudon Co., Va., in Lancaster Co., Penn., and in many localities in the Rocky Mountains and Cascade Range.

Epidote
Ca$_2$(AlOH)
(AlFe$_2$) (SiO$_4$)$_3$
Pl. 42
Occurs in grains or columnar masses; hardness, 6.5; specific gravity 3.4; color green, usually a pistachio or yellow-green; luster vitreous; translucent on thin edges.

Rarely epidote occurs in crystals, which belong to the monoclinic system, and may be either short like the diagrams on plate 42 or long and needle-like. The color and hardness will suffice to determine this mineral, as almost no other has the peculiar yellowish-green color which is characteristic of this form.

Epidote occurs primarily in metamorphic rocks at or near the contact with igneous rocks; or it may be a secondary mineral resulting from the weathering of granites, especially along seams. It sometimes occurs with hornblende in highly folded schists, as in New York City. It is often a mineral which has resulted from the alteration of other minerals, as pyroxene, amphibole, biotite, or even feldspars.

It is found at Chester and Athol, Mass., Haddam, Conn., Amity, Munroe and Warwick, N.Y., East Branch, Penn., in the Lake Superior region, in the Rocky Mountains, etc.

Tourmaline ($FeCrNa-KLi)_4Mg_{12}$ $B_6Al_{16}H_8$ $Si_{12}O_{63}$ Pl. 42 & frontispiece — Occurs in three-sided prismatic crystals; hardness, 7; specific gravity, 3.1; colorless, red, green, brown, or black; luster vitreous; transparent on thin edges.

Tourmaline is readily distinguished from other minerals, as it always occurs in long to short prisms, which are three-sided in cross section. There is also a tendency for the sides to be curved as seen on the end view of D, Pl. 42. Frequently the vertical edges of the prism are beveled with one, two or three faces, grouped about each of the three original edges, and there are often striations on the prism faces. The ends are terminated by a low rhombohedron and again there may be a host of modifying faces on the edges and corners of the end. The common varieties are brown or black in color, but occasionally there may occur green, red, yellow or almost any color. When the crystals are perfect, that is free from impurities and without tiny cracks, tourmaline becomes a gem of popularity and value.

Tourmaline is very complex in composition and may vary considerably, the sodium, potassium, lithium, magnesium, and iron being either more or less abundant or even lacking. The color is to some extent dependent on the proportions of these elements present, the dark varieties having more iron, and the light colored tourmalines lacking it. This mineral is one of those which form from superheated vapors, escaping from molten magmas. It will therefore occur in veins, often associated with copper minerals, in crystalline limestones, or in cavities in granites, where it is associated with such minerals, as beryl, apatite, fluorite, topaz, etc.

If heated tourmaline crystals develop electricity, with the effect of making one end a positive and the other a negative pole, and then will attract bits of straw, ashes, etc. It was first introduced into Europe about 1703 from India, and its vogue as a gem has greatly increased since it was found on Mount Mica near Paris, Me. This Paris, Me., locality was discovered by two boys, amateur mineralogists, Elijah L. Hamlin and Ezekiel Holmes, who in 1820 were returning home from a trip hunting for minerals, when, at the root of a tree, they discovered some gleaming green substance. It proved to be gem-quality tourmaline. A snow storm that night buried their "claim," but next spring it was visited and several fine crystals found. Later this locality was systematically worked, and over $50,000 worth of tourmaline taken from the pegmatite seam in the granite, which lay under the crystals found on the surface. The figure in the frontispiece is one of the crystals from there.

Well known localities are Paris and Hebron, Me., Goshen and Chesterfield, Mass., Acworth and Grafton, N. H., Haddam and Munroe, Conn., Edenville and Port Henry, N. Y., Jefferson Co., Colo., San Diego Co., Calif., etc.

Kaolinite Usually found in whitish clay-
$H_4Al_2Si_2O_9$ like masses; hardness, 2; specific
Kaolin gravity, 2.6; color white to grayish or yellowish; luster dull.

Kaolinite does not generally occur in crystals, though crystals of microscopic size and monoclinic forms have been found. It is a secondary mineral resulting from the decomposition by weathering of feldspars, the calcium, potassium or sodium having been replaced by water. When found in place it is generally white or nearly white, and is characterized by its greasy feel.

As granites or other feldspar-bearing rocks are weathered away, the kaolin is washed out by water, and with other fine material is carried down into lakes or the sea, where it settles to the bottom and is known as clay. Clay is kaolin with more or less impurities.

Pure kaolin is used for the manufacture of china and white porcelain ware; but when it is impure, especially when it has iron in it, baking causes the product to turn red or brown, so that it is only suitable for making tile, bricks, etc.

It is found almost anywhere that feldspar rocks are, or have been, exposed to weathering.

Talc
H_2Mg_3
$(SiO_3)_4$

Occurs in scales, or in fibrous, scaly or compact masses; hardness, 1; specific gravity, 2.7; color white, gray or pale-green; luster pearly; translucent on thin edges.

This mineral is as soft as any, only graphite and molybdenite being of the same hardness, but both these latter two have a black streak, while the streak of talc is white. The greasy feel is also characteristic. Talc is very seldom found in crystals, but if they are found, they will appear like flakes and have a hexagonal cross section, though in reality they belong to the monoclinic system.

Talc is a secondary mineral which usually results from the exposure of magnesium silicates, such as pyroxenes or amphiboles, to moisture. In this case, in-as-much as the original rocks were metamorphic in origin, the talc therefrom will occur in old metamorphic regions. Some talc is also formed by the action of silica-bearing waters on dolomite. This is likely to be the case near the contact between dolomite and igneous rocks. Talc is closely related to serpentine and likely to be found in the same regions.

Talc has come to have a considerable use. Some of it is compact and then called soapstone, and this was used by the ancient Chinese to make images and ornaments; and our North American Indians used it to make large pots, to serve as containers for liquids. Some of these pots have been carved out with great skill, so as to be fairly light in proportion to what they would hold. Pipes and images were also carved from soapstone. Today we still cut soapstone into slabs to make mantels, laundry tubs and sinks. The scaly and fibrous varieties are ground, and used in making paper, paint, roofing, rubber, soap, crayons, toilet powders, etc. The United States produce and use over half the world's production. our industries requiring over 100,000 tons of talc a year. Of this 38% goes into paper, 23% into paint, 18% into roofing, and so on down to toilet powder which uses $2\frac{1}{2}\%$, or 2,500 tons a year.

Talc is found in metamorphosed regions, that is in New England, all down the east side of the Appalachian Mts., in the Rocky Mts., and the Cascade Ranges, with a large number of local occurrences. New York State is the leading producer.

Serpentine
$H_4Mg_3 Si_2O_9$
Pl. 43
Occurs in compact, granular or fibrous masses; hardness, 3; specific gravity, 2.6; color green; luster greasy; translucent on thin edges. Serpentine is never in crystals. Its color and hardness serve to distinguish it. Like talc it is a secondary mineral resulting from the alteration, in the presence of moisture, of pyroxenes, amphiboles, and especially, olivine. As these are often in metamorphic rocks, the serpentine is likely to be associated with metamorphic rocks. Some serpentine is also the result of the action of silica-bearing water on dolomite, and this is likely to

occur in areas of sedimentary rocks. The fibrous variety of serpentine, *chrysolite*, usually occurs in seams or veins, and when the fibers are long, it is used as asbestos. This form of asbestos is the one most used commercially today, as there are remarkably large deposits of it in the Province of Quebec, which provide the major part of the world supply. In the United States it is also found in California and Arizona but only in moderate quantities.

Massive serpentine is used in considerable quantities as an ornamental stone, the green color varied with streaks and blotches of white, yellow and red, due to various impurities, making it very effective. It is, however, only suitable for interior work as the weather quickly spoils the polished surface. This is further discussed under serpentine rock, page 245.

Serpentine is found at Newfane, Vt., Newburyport, Mass., Brewster, Antwerp, etc., N. Y., Hoboken, N. J., in Pennsylvania, Maryland, etc.

Chlorite
$H_8(MgFe)_5$
$Al_2(SiO_6)_3$
Pl. 43

Occurs in monoclinic crystals of six-sided outline, or in scaly flakes or masses; hardness, 2; specific gravity 2.8; color green; luster pearly on cleavage faces; translucent on thin edges.

Chlorite is a family name, covering a series of closely related minerals, so similar in appearance that they are best considered under this common name. In many respects they resemble mica, in the shape of the crystals and the remarkable basal cleavage. At first glance it is easy to confuse the two, but chlorite scales are not elastic, and when bent, stay bent, instead of snapping back like mica. In fact they look like more or less rotted micas. This is more than appearance, for chlorites form as a result of the alternation of micas in the presence of moisture. They are then secondary, and will be found where mica-rocks have been weathered, as in granites and schists.

They may be expected anywhere that micas have been long exposed, as in New England, the Rocky Mountains, or the Sierra Nevada or Cascade Ranges. Special localities are Brewster, N. Y., Unionville and Texas, Penn., etc.

THE ZEOLITES

The zeolites are a group of white minerals, with a pearly luster, light weight, and easy solubility in acids; which, because their contained water is lightly held, readily boil before the blowpipe. They are all secondary minerals, which result from the decomposition of feldspars, when exposed to weathering. They are almost universally found in seams and cavities of disintegrating lavas. From a group of a dozen or so, three are common enough to be considered here. They may be found by watching such places, as where trap rock is being quarried for road material, or being blasted for any reason.

Analcite
$Na_2Al_2Si_4\ O_{12}$
$+ 2H_2O$
Pl. 44

Occurs as trapezohedrons in seams and cavities in lavas; hardness, 5.5; specific gravity, 2.2; colorless, white or pink; luster vitreous; transparent on thin edges.

Analcite usually occurs in the 24-sided form, known as a trapezohedron, as illustrated in figure A, Pl. 44; but it may also occur in cubes with the three faces of the trapezohedron on each corner. Small crystals are often colorless, but the larger ones are either white or pink, and are opaque. While the form is the same as that of garnets, the color, lesser hardness, and the occurrence in lavas will serve to distinguish this mineral. If placed in hydrochloric acid analcite dissolves to a gelatinous mass.

It is always found in seams and cavities in lavas, as at Bergen Hill and Weehawken, N. J., Westfield, Mass., in the Lake Superior region, etc

Natrolite
$Na_2Al_2Si_3 O_{10}$
$+ 2H_2O$
Plate 44

Occurs as bristling crystals in seams and cavities in lavas; hardness, 5.5; specific gravity, 2.2; colorless; luster vitreous; transparent on thin edges.

Natrolite occurs as beautiful bristling tufts of needle-like crystals, each crystal an orthorhombic prism with a very low pyramid on the end. This mineral is so easily fusible that it can be melted in a candle flame, giving to the flame the characteristic yellow color due to sodium. In hydrochloric acid it dissolves to a gelatinous mass. It is always a secondary mineral in cavities and seams in disintegrating lavas, and the tuft-like manner of growth is so characteristic, that once seen, it will always be recognized.

Natrolite is found at Weehawken and Bergen Hill, N. J., at Westfield, Mass., in the Lake Superior region, etc.

Stilbite
$H_4(CaNa_2)$
$Al_2(SiO_3)_6$
$+ 4H_2O$
Pl. 44

Usually occurs in sheaf-like bundles of fibrous crystals; hardness, 5.5; specific gravity 2.2; colorless to white, yellow or brown; luster vitreous; transparent on thin edges.

Stilbite crystals are really monoclinic, but on account of almost universal twinning, appear as if orthorhombic. Like the two foregoing minerals, stilbite is found in the seams and cavities of disintegrating lavas. It is readily recognized by its habit of forming in sheaf-like bundles of fibrous crystals. It may also, but more rarely, occur in radiating masses. In hydrochloric acid it is completely dissolved. It is found in lavas, at Weehawken and Bergen Hill, N. J., in the Lake Superior region, etc.

CALCIUM

Calcium is one of the most abundant of metals, but never occurs as such in nature, nor is it used as a metal by man. In its metallic form it is yellowish-white, and intermediate between lead and gold in hardness. Exposed to air it soon tarnishes by oxidation, and in water rapidly decomposes the water, forming the oxide. However, it has a great affinity for other elements, and makes a large number of minerals, the most important of which are calcite, aragonite, gypsum and fluorite, while it is an essential component of some garnets, anorthite, epidote, amphibole and pyroxene. It is very widely distributed as limestone, and is found in solution in most all natural waters, and in the shells and bones of many animals and some plants.

Calcite
CaCo₃
Pl. 45

Occurs in well defined crystals, in incrustations, and in stalactitic, oolitic, and granular masses; hardness, 3; specific gravity 2.7; colorless to white, or when impure, yellow, brown, green, red or blue; luster vitreous to dull; transparent on thin edges.

Next to quartz, calcite is the most abundant of all minerals, and occurs in an almost endless variety of forms, over 300 having been described. It belongs to the hemihedral section of the hexagonal system, the form of the crystals being all sorts of variations of the rhombohedron, and combinations of left and right handed rhombohedrons. The cleavage is entirely uniform, in three directions, parallel to the faces of the rhombohedron, and at an angle of 74° 55′ with each other. Crystals may occur in the form characteristic of the cleavage, but not often. The commonest forms are a more or less elongated scalenohedron, made by combining right and left handed rhombohedrons, so that the resulting pyramid is six-sided, as in figure C, Plate 45. Such a scalenohedron may be combined with other forms in a great variety of ways. The six-sided prism with the ends terminated by one or more sets of rhombohedral faces is also fairly common. Twinning occurs occasionally.

The quickest way to determine calcite is by the hardness (3), combined with the fact that it effervesces, when hydrochloric acid is dropped upon it.

An interesting feature of this mineral is its marked property of deflecting light rays, so that a line or object placed behind a piece of clear calcite appears double. It was with pieces of calcite from Iceland that this was first seen; so that large transparent crystals of calcite are still called *Iceland spar;* and such calcite is used to make the Nichol's prisms for microscopes, which are so useful in the study of minerals. This power of refracting light is present in all minerals, but not to such a marked degree as in calcite. The elongated scalenohedrons of calcite are often called "dog-toothed spar" from a fancied resemblance between them and the dog's tooth.

Calcite is present in solution in the water of the sea and most streams, from which it is withdrawn by many animals and some plants, to make their shells, and bones. The foramenifera, some sponges, the echinoderms, corals and molluscs all draw large quantities from the water in which they live, and build more or less permanent structures from it. These shells when they fall to the bottom, or after being broken to bits, accumulate on the bottom and make limestone, which is widely distributed over the country. This same limestone, when metamorphosed and crystalline, is marble.

Calcite then is readily soluble in water, and streams flowing along crevices and fissures in limestone dissolve out great cavities or caves, like the Mammoth Cave of Kentucky. Other water, percolating through the limestone, comes to these cavities saturated with lime in solution and drips from the roofs and walls; then as part of the water evaporates, it deposits part of its lime in icicle-like masses, hanging from the roof.

Such masses of non-crystalline calcite are called *stalactites*. Below on the floor of the cave, conical masses are built up in the same manner where the dripping water falls on the floor. These are *stalagmites*. In these limestone caves and in smaller cavities many of the most beautiful crystals grow. Somewhat similarly, when hot water from deep springs comes to the surface, it cools and can not carry as much lime, and so around the spring is laid down layer after layer of non-crystalline calcite making a mass known as *travertine*. Sometimes this is colored by iron or other impurities and a banded effect results. Such travertine as the "Suisun marble" from California, "California onyx," "Mexican onyx," and "satin spar" all belong to this class.

The coral animals, especially in tropical waters precipitate an enormous amount of lime, until whole reefs are built of lime in this non-crystalline form. In places it is hundreds of feet thick and hundreds of miles in extent. Some of this coral has become popular for personal adornment. This is particularly a small, fine-grained variety, *Corallum rubrum*, which lives almost exclusively in the Mediterranean Sea. This coral is red in color, varying all the way from a deep red to white. It grows in small masses, three pounds being a good sized mass, in water 60 to 100 feet deep, requires some ten years to develop a full-sized mass. The making of this into beads and ornaments is an Italian industry. The demand is growing, while at the same time the supply is diminishing, and search is being widely made for more such coral, but up to the present time with little success. This precious coral is much worn as a protection against the "evil eye" and is widely imitated, apparently with as much protection to the wearer. When coral beads are offered cheap, they are probably something else, red gypsum being much used. This and all imitations can be readily detected by trying a drop of acid in the bead. Coral will effervesce, but gypsum and other substitutes will not.

The bulk of the shells of most molluscs is made of lime, but the mother-of-pearl layer inside is usually aragonite. The chalk of the cliffs on either side of the English channel is lime, and composed of the shells of single celled animals. See p. 213. When lime is deposited in loose porous masses, as around grass, etc., and below hot springs, this mass is termed *calcareous tufa*.

Calcite will be found almost everywhere, some of the localities for the finest crystals being Antwerp and Lockport, N. Y., Middletown, Conn., the caves of Kentucky, Warsaw, Ill., Joplin, Mo., Hazel Green, Wis., etc.

Aragonite
CaCO₃
Pl. 46

Occurs in crystals, in columnar or fibrous masses, or incrustations; hardness, 3.5; specific gravity, 2.9; colorless, white or amber; luster vitreous; transparent on thin edges.

Aragonite has the same chemical composition as calcite, but it crystallizes in the orthorhombic system, either in simple forms like A on Plate 46, or twinned, so as to make forms which seem hexagonal. When in simple crystals its form easily distinguishes it from calcite and dolomite, but when twinned it appears much like either of these two minerals. From calcite it can then be distinguished by its greater hardness and the fact that it has cleavage in one direction only, and that imperfect. The cleavage is the only easy method of distinguishing it from dolomite. However, aragonite is most always easily distinguished by its habits, for it generally forms long slender crystals, which appear more like fibers than crystals. Neither calcite nor dolomite is at all fibrous.

Aragonite is much less abundant than calcite, and has resulted, either from deposition from hot waters, or from waters having sulphates in solution as well as lime. Much of the travertine, and many stalagmites and stalactites are composed of aragonites, forming as outlined under calcite. The mother-of-pearl layer in the shells of bivalves is generally aragonite. The pearly luster of this layer is due to its being formed by the successive deposition of one thin layer upon another; so that light falling on the mother-of-pearl, penetrates, part of it to one layer and part to another, and is then reflected. Certain molluscs have this layer composed of especially thin layers, one, the *Unios* or freshwater clams, the other, the "pearl oysters" or *Aviculidæ*, these latter, however, being only distantly related to the edible oysters. In the cases, where molluscs of either of these two families are of large size, large pieces of mother-of-pearl can be recovered, and are used for buttons, handles, and various ornamental objects. A further peculiarity of these same molluscs is the formation of pearls in the sheet of flesh, lining the shells. The pearls are round or rounded concretions of aragonite. At the center there is a grain of sand, or more often a tiny dead parasite. Either was an irritant to the mollusc, and to be rid of it, a layer of aragonite was secreted around it. Then as the mollusc continued to grow and secrete layers for its shell, it also added each time another layer around the sand-grain or parasite, until in time a pearl of noticeable, and then of considerable size resulted. These have all the pearly luster of the mother-of-pearl in a sphere which tends to make the luster even more marked.

Pearls were in use as ornaments in China some twenty-three centuries before Christ, and in India over 500 B.C. They were very highly prized by the Romans and since their times the rulers of India have shown a remarkable fondness for them. Today the finest come from the Gulf of Persia and the Red Sea, while still others are found about Australia and in the Caribbean Sea. In the United States not a few are collected every year from the fresh water clams, some of them beautifully tinted with pink or yellow.

Aragonite is found widely, as at Haddam, Conn., Edenville, N. Y., Hoboken, N. J., New Garden, Penn., Warsaw, Ill., etc.

Anhydrite
$CaSO_4$
Pl. 46

Occurs in cleavable or granular masses, rarely in crystals; hardness, 3–3.5; specific gravity, 2.9; color white, gray, bluish or reddish; luster pearly on cleavage faces; transparent on thin edges.

When anhydrite occurs in crystals, they are orthorhombic, like the diagram on Plate 46. Usually, however, it is found in beds or layers, which were deposited by the evaporation of sea water, and so it is associated with salt. Anhydrite has three cleavage planes which are at right angles to one another, which produce rectangular or cube-like forms. Mostly anhydrite is associated with gypsum, from which it differs by its greater hardness, pseudo-cubic cleavage, and the fact that anhydrite is not readily soluble in acid, while gypsum is. Chemically it differs from gypsum in not having water of crystallization, which gypsum does have. The anhydrite is likely to occur as veins and irregular masses in beds of gypsum. Calcium sulphate is precipitated from sea water when 37% of the water has been evaporated, and it may be deposited either as anhydrite or as gypsum, the factors, which decide as to which of these two minerals it will be, being as yet unknown. After deposition, if exposed to moisture, the anhydrite may change to gypsum, irregular masses often remaining unchanged.

It is found in salt mines in Elsworth Co., Kan., in limestone cavities at Lockport, N. Y., in veins in Shasta Co., Calif., etc

Gypsum
$CaSO_4 + 2H_2O$
Pl. 47

Occurs in crystals, in cleavable masses, or in fibrous masses; hardness, 2; specific gravity, 2.3; colorless, white, amber, gray, or pink; luster vitreous, silky or pearly; transparent on thin edges.

Gypsum crystals are monoclinic as seen on

Plate 47, the perfect ones usually occurring in clay, as at Oxford, O., or in cavities; while crystals of less perfect outline, but with fine cleavages, are found in Utah, Kansas, and Colorado. The cleavage is very perfect in one direction, making it possible to strip off thin sheets almost like mica, and less perfect in two other directions, which appear on the smooth surface of the first cleavage as lines intersecting at 66° 14′. Twinning is also common in such a way, that the two united crystals make forms similar to arrowheads. These cleavages and the twinning show nicely in the photograph of gypsum on Plate 47.

Gypsum is distinguished from anhydrite by its lesser hardness, its cleavage and by being soluble in acids.

Most gypsum occurs in beds or granular masses which were deposited from evaporating sea-water, coming down when 37% of the water was lost. Such beds are often very extensive and are quarried as a source of gypsum to make plaster of Paris, stucco, neat plaster, Keene's cement, plaster and wall board, partition tiles, etc. The use of the gypsum for plaster of Paris and all these other uses is based on its affinity for water of crystallization. The gypsum is first heated to about 400° C., which drives off the water of crystallization, and causes it to crumble to a powder, which is the plaster of Paris. When water is added, it is taken up and the powder "sets," or recrystallizes back to gypsum. This simple reaction has made it very useful, for making moulds, casts, hard finish on walls, as stucco, etc.

When the granular type of gypsum is fine

grained, it is known as *alabaster*, which is used for carving vases, statuettes, ornaments, etc. The fibrous variety is called *satin spar*, and is sometimes used for cheap jewelry and ornaments, but it is very soft and quickly wears out. At Niagara Falls there is a considerable trade in objects carved from this satin spar, tourists buying them on the assumption that the mineral is native and comes from under the falls. Most of it, however, comes from Wales, the small amount of gypsum of that region being mostly granular.

Gypsum is found all across the United States, as in New York, Michigan, Virginia, Ohio, Alabama, South Dakota, Wyoming, Colorado, Utah, California, etc.

THE STRONTIUM GROUP

Strontium is a pale-yellow metal, ductile and malleable, but oxidizing quickly when exposed to the air. It does not occur in its native state in Nature, but always as some compound, usually either the carbonate or sulphate. It resembles barium, but differs in giving to the flame a brilliant red color, on which account the compounds of strontium are used mostly in making red fire in fireworks.

Strontianite
$SrCO_3$
Occurs in needle-like crystals, or in columnar or fibrous masses; hardness, 3.5–4; specific gravity, 3.6; color white, pale-green or pale shades of yellow; luster vitreous; transparent on thin edges.

Strontianite is orthorhombic, but appears as if hexagonal, since its general habit is to have three twin crystals grow together in such a way as to make a six-sided double pyramid. In this it is very like witherite, both these minerals appearing externally much alike. They can be readily distinguished, however, by holding a piece in the flame. If it gives a red color to the flame it is strontianite, if green, it is witherite. It effervesces readily in hydrochloric acid.

Strontianite is found in veins and cavities in limestone, where it has been deposited after being leached from the limestone by percolating waters. Though known at several localities it is not now being mined in this country, what we use being imported mostly from Germany.

It is found at Schoharie, Chaumont Bay and Theresa, N. Y., in Mifflin Co., Penn., etc.

Celestite
$SrSO_4$

Occurs in crystals, cleavable masses and fibrous; hardness, 3; specific gravity, 3.9; colorless, white, pale-blue, or reddish; luster vitreous; transparent on thin edges.

Celestite, the sulphate of strontium, is very like barite in external appearance and habit. It is orthorhombic and occurs in tabular crystals. Its cleavage is perfect on the basal plane, and imperfect in one other direction. The ready way of distinguishing celestite from barite is to hold a piece in the flame. If it is celestite it will color the flame red, if barite, green.

Celestite is mostly found in veins or cavities in limestone, where it has been deposited by percolating waters, after having been leached from the limestone. Some years ago an important deposit of celestite was found on Strontian Island in Lake Erie, but that was soon worked out and now no veins are being worked in this country. It is also found at Chaumont Bay, Schoharie and Lockport, N. Y., in Kansas, Texas, West Virginia, Tennessee, etc.

THE BARIUM GROUP

Barium is another metal which does not occur in its native state in Nature. It has only been isolated as a yellow powder, which, exposed to air or water, soon changes to one of the oxides. Both barium and its compounds are peculiar in causing a green color, whenever exposed to the flame. Two of its compounds are fairly abundant, the sulphate, barite, and the carbonate, witherite. The former is the more abundant and has come to be fairly widely used, something over 100,000 tons being annually consumed in the United States, to make the body in flat finish paints for interior work and light colors, for a filler in rubber goods, linoleum, oil cloth, glazed paper, and for a wide range of chemical compounds.

Barite
$BaSO_4$
Pl. 48
heavy spar

Occurs in crystals or in lamellar, nodular or granular masses; hardness 3; specific gravity, 4.5; colorless, white or almost any color; luster vitreous; transparent on thin edges.

Barite occurs in orthorhombic crystals, which are tabular in form, and usually have the edges beveled, as in figure A, Plate 48. There is cleavage in three directions, a rather perfect basal cleavage, and two less perfect cleavages, which are at right angles to the basal cleavage plane, and intersect each other at 78°.

The tabular form, the cleavage, the heavy weight, and the fact that a piece of barite put into the flame colors it green, all serve to distinguish this mineral.

Barite is a secondary mineral of aqueous origin, which has been deposited in veins and cavities in igneous, metamorphic, or sometimes sedimentary rocks. It is most likely to occur in veins in igneous or metamorphic rocks, the barium having been dissolved from certain feldspars and micas by percolating water, and then redeposited in the fissures, as the water came into them. If in sedimentary rocks, the barite veins are usually in limestones. Barite is quite likely to be a gangue mineral for the ores of lead.

It is found at Hatfield and Leverett, Mass., Cheshire, Conn., Pillar Point, N. Y., Cartersville, Ga., in Virginia, North Carolina, South Carolina, Missouri, Kentucky, Tennessee, Alabama, Illinois, Wisconsin, Nevada, California, Alaska, etc.

Witherite
$BaCO_3$
Pl. 48

Occurs in crystals, or in granular or columnar masses; hardness, 3.5; specific gravity, 4.3; color white to gray, luster vitreous; translucent on thin edges.

Witherite is not an abundant mineral. Its crystals are really orthorhombic, but they are usually twinned, three crystals growing through each other in such a manner that the resulting crystal appears like a six-sided double pyramid, similar to the one figured on Plate 48. The commonest mode of occurrence is in compact masses. Witherite effervesces when cold acid is dropped upon it, which, with its heavy weight, and the green color it gives to the flame, serves to distinguish the mineral. It is used for medicines, in chemical industries, and a considerable amount is made into rat poisons. The chief locality for witherite is in northern England, but in this country it is found along with barite, especially at Lexington, Ky., and in Michigan.

CARBON

Carbon is an element widely distributed in nature, occasionally appearing in its elementary form, as graphite or the diamond, but much more important in its compounds. Small quantities are present in the air as carbon dioxide, CO_2, immense quantities occurring in the carbonate minerals, which have been considered under their respective metallic salts, as calcite, malachite, siderite, cerrusite, smithsonite, witherite, etc., and still other large quantities being represented in organic compounds, which occur as rocks under the heads of petroleum, coal, etc. The occurrence of limestones, graphite, coal or petroleum is always indicative of the activity of living organisms, and in some cases is the only indication of life in the earlier rocks.

Graphite
C
Plumbago
Occurs in hexagonal scales or flakes, in layered masses, or earthy lumps; hardness, 1; specific gravity, 2.1; color black or steel-gray; streak gray; luster metallic; opaque on thin edges.

Like the diamond graphite is pure carbon, but in this case it is in non-crystalline form. It occurs in both igneous and metamorphic rocks. In the former case it is either in flakes in the rock, or in veins, and has been derived directly from the molten magmas, having either precipitated in the hardening granite or lava, or having been carried into the fissures and there precipitated to make the veins of graphite. In either case the graphite probably represents organic deposits which have been melted into the igneous magma at the time of its formation. Graphite may also occur in metamorphic rocks, beds of coal or other organic deposits being altered by the heat. Such beds are often of considerable extent and economic importance.

The extreme softness, greasy feel, and the dark-gray streak readily distinguish graphite.

It is widely used in making crucibles and furnace linings for foundries, lead pencils, paint, lubricating powders, etc.

Graphite is found at Brandon, Vt., Sturbridge, Mass., Ashford, Conn., in Essex, Warren and Washington Cos., N. Y., Clay, Chilton and Coosa Cos., Ala., Raton, N. M., Dillon, Mont., etc.

**Diamond
C**

Occurs in octahedral crystals; hardness, 10; specific gravity, 3.5; colorless to yellow, brown, blue, etc., luster adamantine; transparent on thin edges.

Like graphite the diamond is pure carbon, but in this case in crystal form. It is the hardest of all minerals, and as brilliant as any; so that in spite of being by no means the rarest, it may easily be considered the most popular of all gems. Tiny diamonds have been made artificially under great heat and pressure; so that this mineral is thought of as forming in Nature in dark igneous lavas at great depths. The diamond has good cleavage parallel to the octahedron faces, and, in spite of some traditions to the contrary, is brittle.

There are not many diamond localities, the most famous being the Kimberley district of South Africa, which produces many times as many diamonds as all the others put together, though all the time some are being found in Borneo and Brazil. A very few have been found in the United States, only one locality however yielding them in the original matrix. That is at Murfreesboro, Ark., where they are mined in a disintegrating peridotite (a dark lava, mostly peridot), which has been extruded through the sedimentary rocks of that region. This matrix is similar to the "blue earth," the matrix of the diamonds of South Africa, which occurs in "pipes," representing the necks of ancient volcanoes. The American diamonds are of small size, averaging considerably less than a third of a carat in weight, which does not allow great value to the individual diamonds.

From time to time, especially large diamonds have been found in different parts of the world, the largest being the Cullinan diamond, found at the Premier Diamond Mine of South Africa. It weighed 3025 carats or about a pound and a quarter, and was valued at over $3,000,000. It

was presented to King Edward VII, who had it
cut into 11 brilliants, four of which are larger
than any other diamond yet found. Other famous diamonds, like the Kohinoor, 106 carats,
found in India in 1304; the Regent, 136 carats,
also found in India; the Orloff, 193 carats, set in
the eye of an Indian idol; the South Star, 125
carats, the largest ever found in Brazil; the blue
Hope, etc., have in many cases romantic and
interesting stories woven about them.

Though for ages diamonds have been highly
prized gems, it is only in comparatively recent
times that cutting and polishing have been resorted to, for the purpose of enhancing their
brilliancy. This is done by grinding reflecting
faces on the original stone, by the aid of discs of
iron or tin in which diamond dust has been embedded. Diamond chips and cloudy or imperfect
diamonds are used for making tools for cutting
glass, rock drills, etc.

PHOSPHORUS

The element phosphorus at ordinary temperatures is an almost colorless, faintly yellow, solid
substance of glistening appearance and waxy
consistency. In Nature it does not occur pure,
but always as one of its compounds. It is of
great importance to man for it is one of the essen-
tials for plant growth and also for the higher
animals, being required for the bones and to some
extent for nervous tissue. Originally it is found
in all the igneous rocks. Some of the phosphorus
is removed by solution and carried to other re-

gions and to the sea. From this distribution it comes into the sedimentary rocks, and, when they are altered by heat, into the metamorphic rocks. Thus it has a wide, though by no means even, distribution. The soils formed by disintegration of these rocks probably all have some phosphorus in them; but where there is vigorous plant growth, it soon tends to become exhausted, and must be renewed. For this reason the use of phosphates has become of prime importance in Agriculture. The possession of beds of rock carrying phosphorus has come to be of international importance. The United States is particularly fortunate in this respect, and produces over 25% of the world's supply of phosphates. Most all the phosphorus is recovered either from phosphate minerals, the most important of which is apatite, or from the non-crystalline and impure mixtures of phosphate minerals and other substances, discussed under phosphate rock.

Apatite
$Ca_5F(PO_4)_3$
Pl. 49
Occurs in crystals, concretionary nodules, or in bedded masses; hardness, 5; specific gravity, 3.2; color reddish-brown or green, rarely white or colorless; luster vitreous; translucent on thin edges.

Apatite occurs in hexagonal prisms, usually with the ends truncated by a basal plane, and with one or more sets of pyramidal faces between the prism and the basal plane. Crystals range in size from tiny to over a foot in diameter. There is but one cleavage and that is basal. The crystal form, cleavage, and hardness will easily determine this mineral. Apatite is usually associated with igneous or highly metamorphic rocks, such as granites, gneisses, and crystalline limestones. While the phosphoric acid of apatite is highly desirable for use in fertilizers, the crystals do not occur in sufficient abundance to make them commercially available, and non-crystalline phosphate rocks are resorted to for this purpose.

Crystals of apatite are found at Norwich and Bolton, Mass., Rossie and Edenville, N. Y., Suckasunny and Hurdstown, N. J., Leiperville, Penn., Wilmington, Del., etc. Templeton, Canada, is perhaps the best known locality for fine apatite.

Turquois
$H_5[Al(OH)_2]$
$Cu(OH)(PO_4)_4$
Occurs in seams and incrustations; hardness, 6; specific gravity, 2.7; color bluish-green; streak blue; luster waxy; translucent to opaque on thin edges.

In this country this complex phosphate of aluminum and copper is found in streaks and patches in volcanic rocks, but in Persia comes from metamorphic rocks. To the Persians it was a magical stone, protecting the wearer from injuries, and among the Pueblo Indians it was regarded as of religious value in warding off evil. The best turquois comes from Persia, but it has been found at several points in the United States, as in Los Cerrillos and Burro Mts., N. M., in Mohave Co., Ariz., San Bernardino Co., Cal., in Nevada and Colorado.

FLUORINE

At ordinary temperatures the element fluorine is a colorless gas, which was not obtained pure until 1888, because it could not be contained in vessels of glass, gold, platinum, etc. At that time it was made and kept in a vessel composed of an alloy of platinum and iridium. Its most important compound is hydrofluoric acid, a fuming liquid, which is mostly used to etch or dissolve glass. It occurs in several minerals, like tourmaline, turquois, etc., but the only one used to obtain the hydrofluoric acid is fluorite.

Fluorite   Occurs in crystals and cleavable
CaF₂, Pl. 50   masses; hardness, 4; specific gravity,
Fluor spar   3.2; colorless or some shade of violet, green, yellow, or rose; luster vitreous; transparent on thin edges.

Fluorite usually occurs in beautiful cubic crystals, often with the edges and corners beveled by smaller faces, and occasionally in twins, which seem to have grown through each other. There is perfect cleavage parallel to each of the octahedral faces, which often, as in the illustration on Plate 50, show as cracks cutting off the corners.

Since fluorite loses weight and color on heating, it is concluded that the colors are due to the presence of hydrocarbon compounds. The red and the green fluorite when heated to above 212° F. become phosphorescent, as may be seen if they are thus heated and exposed to the light, then taken into the dark.

Fluorite is quite commonly the gangue mineral

associated with metallic ores, and is also likely to occur with topaz, apatite, etc. It is generally in such places that it seems to have been deposited from hot vapors, rising from igneous magmas.

It is the only mineral at all common from which fluorine can be obtained, and is used for making hydrofluoric acid, and other chemical compounds of this element. It is, however, of much greater importance as a flux in reducing iron, silver, lead and copper ores. In the industries it finds a place, being used to make apochromatic lenses, cheap jewelry, and for the electrodes in flaming arc lamps.

Fluorite is widely distributed, some of the better known localities being Trumbull and Plymouth, Conn., Rossie and Muscalonge Lake, N. Y., Gallatin Co., Ill., Thunder Bay, Lake Superior, Missouri, etc.

Halite
NaCl, Pl. 50
Salt
Occurs in crystals, and in cleavable and granular masses; hardness, 2.5; specific gravity, 2.1; colorless to white; luster vitreous; transparent on thin edges.

Halite is common salt, occurring in cubic crystals, with perfect cubic cleavage. Its form, hardness, taste, and solubility in water make it easy to determine.

Halite is the most abundant salt in sea water, making about 2.5% out of the total of 3.5% of solids in solution. It is also a prominent, when not the leading, salt in solution in the waters of inland lakes, like Great Salt Lake, or the Dead Sea, there being 20% of halite in the former and

8% in the latter, though the total of solid in solution in the water of the Dead Sea is greater than that in Great Salt Lake.

The great salt deposits are mostly the result of the evaporation of the water of arms or isolated portions of former oceans; the salt, gypsum, etc., left by the drying sea, having been buried beneath later sediments. Other bodies of salt represent the disappearance of ancient lakes. There are also the curious "salt domes" of Louisiana and Texas, which are immense, roughly circular, subterranean masses of salt extending to as yet unknown depths which are thought to have been formed by masses of salt from some deep source bed pushing their way upward through the overlying formations by plastic flowage. As the upthrust took place the sediments were arched into domes. Some of these domes are today important sources of rock salt.

There are extensive beds of salt under parts of New York, Michigan, Ohio, Oklahoma, Kansas, etc., which are mostly worked by drilling wells into the salt layer, then introducing hot water to dissolve the salt. The brine thus formed is pumped to the surface, and the salt recovered by evaporation in pans. During the process, skeleton crystals of salt with concave faces may form, but in Nature the crystals are uniformly solid cubes.

Boracite
$Mg_7Cl_2B_{16}O_{30}$ Occurs in small crystals or granular masses; hardness of crystals, 7; of the masses, 4.5; specific gravity 3; colorless to white; luster vitreous; transparent to translucent on thin edges.

Small crystals, associated with salt and gypsum, occur in the beds and incrustations, which result from the drying up of alkaline lakes, especially in Nevada and southern California. The crystals are orthorhombic, but appear like perfect cubes, with the edges beveled and part of the corners cut. They are not easily dissolved in water, but quickly go into solution in hydrochloric acid.

Colemanite Occurs in crystals or compact
$Ca_2B_6O_{11}$ masses; hardness, 4.5; specific grav-
$+5H_2O$ ity, 2.4; colorless to white; luster
vitreous; translucent on thin edges.

The crystals when they occur, are monoclinic; but usually colemanite is a bedded deposit, which has resulted from the drying up of a saline lake. It was first found in Death Valley, Cal., in 1882, then near Dagget, Cal., and since then in several similar locations in Nevada and Oregon. The deposits are of all grades of purity, the colemanite being mixed with varying quantities of mud. Today this mineral is the chief source of borax, which is used in medicines, cosmetics, colored glazes, enamel, and as a preservative.

Borax Occurs in crystals or in powdery
$NaB_4O_7 +$ incrustations; hardness, 2; specific
$10H_2O$ gravity, 1.7; colorless to white;
luster vitreous; translucent on thin edges.

The crystals are tiny and monoclinic, this mineral being usually obtained by the evaporation of the saline waters of such lakes as Clear and Borax Lakes in southern California, or from the muds of salt marshes, like Searles Borax Marsh in California. Originally most of our borax came from a large saline lake in Tibet, but now most of it is obtained from colemanite. Borax is soluble in water, giving it a sweetish taste.

Sulphur
S. Pl. 51

Occurs in crystals, incrustations or compact masses; hardness, 2; specific gravity, 2; color yellow; streak yellow; luster resinous; translucent on thin edges.

Aside from the numerous compounds, such as the sulphides of the metals like pyrite, galena, spalerite, etc., and the sulphates, like gypsum, barite, anglesite, etc., sulphur occurs in its elemental form in Nature. In this case it may be in crystals, which are orthorhombic and usually occur as octahedrons, with the upper and lower ends truncated, either by a basal plane, or by a lower octahedron, or by both. Incrustations and compact masses are, however, much the commoner mode of occurrence. The incrustations are found mostly about volcanic regions, where the sulphur has risen from the molten lavas as a sublimate, and on cooling has been deposited in crevices or on the adjacent surfaces. Irregular masses of sulphur are often found where sulphide minerals, like pyrite or galena have been decomposed in such a way as to leave the sulphur behind. The extensive beds of sulphur are usually associated with gypsum, and are thought to be the result of water, containing bituminous matter, so acting on gypsum as to remove the calcium and oxygen as lime, and leave the sulphur. Finally many waters carry sulphates in solution, from which the sulphur may be precipitated by certain sulphur bacteria, making thus incrustations on the bottom of ponds or lakes.

Sulphur is used for making matches, gunpowder, fireworks, insecticides, in medicine, vulcanizing rubber, etc. It is widely distributed, however, most of the present world's production is from deposits associated with the "salt domes" of Texas and Louisiana. A "caprock" of gypsum and anhydrite overlies many of these which often contains elemental sulphur. Wells are drilled into this, and the sulphur is melted by the introduction of hot steam. This melted sulphur is then pumped to the surface and run into molds.

Some of the best known localities are Sulphurdale, Utah, Cody and Thermopolis, Wyo., Santa Barbara Co., Cal., Humbolt Co., Nev., and about the hot springs of the Yellowstone Park.

Ice **H₂O, Pl. 51** *water*   Occurs solid as ice, snow and frost, or liquid as water; hardness, 2; specific gravity, .92; colorless to white; luster adamantine; transparent on thin edges.

Though we seldom think of ice, and its liquid form, water, as a mineral, still it is one, and perhaps the most important of all minerals, as well as the most common. Ice melts at 32° F. and vaporizes at 212° F., being then termed steam. Because it is so common and liquid at ordinary temperatures it acts as a solvent for a host of other minerals, and is therefore the agent by which they are transported from place to place and redeposited in veins and beds.

Not only does water act as a transportation agent for minerals in solution, but is also the agent of erosion and weathering. Water vaporizes slowly when exposed to the air at all temperatures above freezing, and so it is slowly rising from the surface of the sea or lakes or moist ground into the air, where it would accumulate until the air was saturated, if the air would only keep still and at a uniform temperature. The air will hold a given amount of water vapor, which is, for example, 17 grams per cubic meter when the temperature is 68° F., but at 59° F. it will hold only $12\frac{1}{2}$ grams, or at 50° F. only 9 grams. Thus the air is more or less completely saturated at higher temperatures, and when the temperature is lowered the air can not hold all it has taken up, and it is precipitated in dew, rain or snow, most often as rain. When the rain falls it mechanically carries away, and more or less slowly transports to other places particles of rock, being thus the agent of erosion; and when it is slowed down, as on entering the quiet water of a lake or the sea, it drops the mechanically carried sediment and makes sedimentary deposits.

Another very important and unique feature of water is that on freezing it expands about $\frac{1}{11}$th of its former bulk, so that, as a result, ice floats, and also wherever water in crevices is frozen, the crevices are enlarged. In locations where this freezing and melting take place repeatedly throughout a year, there the breaking up of rocks is rapid.

This is hardly the place to take up a complete discussion of water, but its action as a solvent, mechanically, and in freezing, melting, and vaporizing is the basis of a large part of the study of geology.

When water crystallizes, as in forming ice, it is in the hexagonal system. It tends to twinning and a snow-flake is made up of a large number of twinned crystals, each diverging from the other at 60°. When ice is formed in the air or on the surface of water it forms these complex and beautiful multiple twins, of which but a couple are suggested here. Beneath the surface the hexagonal crystals grow downward into the water, parallel to each other, making a fibrous structure, which is very apparent when ice is "rotten," which is the time at which the surfaces of the prisms are separating, because the molecules leave the crystal in the reverse order to which they united with it. Frost in marshy or spongy ground will often show this fibrous growth beautifully.

CHAPTER IV

THE ROCKS

Broadly speaking a rock is an essential part of the crust of the earth, and includes loose material, like sand, mud, or volcanic ashes, as well as compact and solid masses, like sandstone and granite. Rocks are aggregates of minerals, either several minerals grouped together, as are mica, quartz and feldspar to make granite, or large quantities of a single mineral, like quartz grains to make sandstone.

The rocks are most conveniently classified according to their mode of origin, into three main groups, igneous, sedimentary, and metamorphic. The igneous rocks are those which have solidified from a molten magma, like lavas, granites, etc. The sedimentary rocks are those which represent accumulations of fragments or grains, derived from various sources, usually the weathering of other rocks, and deposited by such agents as water, wind and organisms. Metamorphic rocks are those which were originally either igneous or sedimentary, but have been altered by the actions of heat, pressure and water, so that the primary character has been changed, often to such an extent as to be obscured.

Rocks once formed in any of the above ways are being constantly altered in character by the various processes of nature. Those exposed on the surface are weathered to pieces, and the fragments are transported by wind or water to accumulate elsewhere as sedimentary rocks. Those buried deep beneath the surface are affected by the high temperature and pressure of the depths of the earth and thus metamorphosed. For instance a granite exposed on the surface is slowly weathered, some parts being carried away in solution by the rain water, others less soluble remaining as grains of quartz, mica or kaolin. These are transported by water and sorted, the finer kaolin being carried to still and deep water, the quartz and mica accumulating in some lowland as sand. This sand will in time be cemented to a sandstone, later slowly buried beneath the surface. If buried deep it will feel the effect of the interior temperature, which increases as one goes down at the rate of one degree F. for every 50 feet. If this should be in a region where folding and mountain-making takes place, the material under the folds would be melted (because of the relief from pressure which would permit the high temperature to act freely) and become igneous rock, either coming to the surface as lava, or remaining below the surface and making a granite or similar rock; while the sedimentary material not melted but near enough to the molten material to be affected, would be metamorphosed, in this case to a quartzite. Much of the interest and profit in studying rocks, will come from the understanding which they will give as to the history of that particular part of the earth's crust where they are found.

IGNEOUS ROCKS

Igneous rocks are those which have formed from material that has been melted, which involves temperatures around 1300° C.; or, if there is water in the original material, temperatures as low as 800° C. will suffice. Considering the increase of temperature to be a degree for every 50 feet downward, this involves the rocks having been at depths of 5 to 10 miles below the surface. While at such depths the temperature must be high enough to melt rocks, the great pressure of the overlying rocks seems to keep them solid; for we know that the center of the earth is solid, as is shown by a variety of observations, such as the rate at which earthquake waves are transmitted through the earth, the lack of tidal effects, etc. However, there is every reason to believe that if the pressure is removed from the rocks which are five to ten miles below the surface, there is heat enough at those depths to melt them. When the crust of the earth is folded, as when mountain ranges are formed, the areas under the arches or upward folds are relieved of pressure. Then those rocks, which are under the arches and are relieved, become molten. The molten magma may well up and fill the space beneath the arch where it would cool again very slowly; or, if there is fissuring during the folding, some of the molten material may be forced out through the fissures and pour out over the surface as lava. Another area in which pressures may be locally relieved is in the region of faulting, where the crust of the earth is broken into blocks, between which there are readjustments, some being tipped one way, some another, some uplifted. Here again there would be areas of relieved pressure and molten magmas would form, some of them solidifying in place, others rising to the surface.

The molten material is termed the **magma,** and when it reaches the surface, great quantities of water vapor and other gases escape: or these gases may even escape from magmas which do not reach the surface, rising through fissures. As these hot vapors pass through the fissures, they are cooled, and may deposit part or all of their dissolved compounds in the fissure, making veins. **Lava** is the magma minus the vapors. Magmas vary greatly from place to place, indicating that they are formed locally and do not come from any general interior reservoir, as has sometimes been suggested.

When the molten magmas escape to the surface, they are termed **extrusive,** and as they spread out in a layer this is termed a **sheet.** This rise and overflow may be quiet, and from time to time one outpouring may follow another making sheet after sheet. Or after one outpouring, the pressure below may cease for a time and allow the lava to solidify and make a cap or cover over the opening. Before more lava can rise, this cover must be removed. This usually happens in an explosive manner, the lava below, with the increasing pressure exerted by its expanding gases, finally exerting enough pressure, so that the cover is broken, or shattered and thrown in thousands of fragments into the air, as happened at Mt. Pelée on the Island of Martinique in 1902. The fragments thrown into the air are often termed volcanic ashes, though this is not a good word for them, for they have not been burned.

In case the molten magmas under the relieved areas do not reach the surface they are termed **intrusive.** Such magmas may remain in the space under a mountain fold, or be forced in fissures part way to the surface. When the magma is forced into more or less vertical cracks and there solidifies, and these are exposed by erosion, they are termed **dikes.** Sometimes the magmas have risen part way to the surface and then pushed their way between two horizontal layers of rock and there hardened, in which case they are termed **sills,** when uncovered. The Palisades along the Hudson River are the exposed edge of a sill. Again the molten magmas may well up and spread between two horizontal layers, but come faster than they can spread horizontally, and then the magma takes the form of a half sphere, and the overlying layers of rock are domed up over it. Such a mass is termed a **laccolith.** In all these cases the mass of igneous rock is only discovered when the overlying rocks have been eroded off. The great mass of molten magma under the arches of mountain ranges simply cools slowly into a granitic type of rock. These masses are exposed when the thousands of feet of overlying rock are eroded off. When these masses are exposed, if of but a few miles in extent, they are called **stocks,** but, if of many miles in length and breadth, they are **batholiths.**

and are very characteristic of the heart of mountain ranges.

In all the above cases the exterior of the molten mass cools first, and forms a shell around the rest. The shell determines the size of the mass. As the cooling continues into the interior, it also solidifies, and as all rocks shrink on cooling, cracks develop, separating the mass into smaller pieces. There is usually no regularity about these cracks and the mass is divided into blocks from six inches to three feet in diameter. However, in some cases, especially in sills and laccoliths where the cooling is slower, the shrinkage may be marked by a regular system of cracks which bound the rock into more or less regular hexagonal columns. The Palisades and the Devil's Tower in Wyoming (See Plate 52) show this structure. The Devil's Tower is the remnant of a laccolith, all except the central core of which has been eroded away. All of the above terms have nothing to do with composition, but refer entirely to the manner of occurrence.

While the igneous rocks are classified according to their composition, the rate at which they cooled has much to do with their texture, and certain names apply to the texture. For instance when the molten lava cools very rapidly, there is no time for the formation of crystals, and the resulting rock is glassy or non-crystalline. If the cooling is slow as in large bodies, crystals have time to form and grow to considerable size as in granites. Between these all grades may occur; and one classification of igneous rocks expresses their rate of cooling, in such terms as the following.

Glassy—lavas which have cooled so quickly that they are without distinct cyrstallization, such as obsidian, pitchstone, etc.

Dense or **felsitic**—lavas which have cooled less rapidly, so that crystals have formed, but in which the crystals are too small to be identified by the unaided eye, such as felsite or basalt.

Porphyritic—magmas from which, in solidifying, one mineral has crystallized out first and the crystals have grown to considerable size, while the rest have remained small.

Granitoid—magmas which have solidified slowly, so that all the minerals have crystallized completely, and the component crystals are large enough to be recognized readily, as in granite.

Fragmental—a term applied to the fragments which have resulted from explosive eruptions of igneous rocks. These fragments may be loose or consolidated. Volcanic ashes are typical.

Porous—a term applied to the lava near the upper surface, which is filled with gas cavities, such as pumice.

Amygdoloidal—is the term applied to porous lavas, when the cavities have been filled by other minerals, such as calcite or some of the zeolites.

In determining a rock, first decide whether it is igneous, sedimentary or metamorphic. The igneous character is recognized by its being either glassy, or composed of masses of crystals irregularly arranged, there being neither layering nor bedding.

When it is located as igneous, turn to the key on page 177 and decide as to which type of tex-

CLASSIFICATION OF IGNEOUS ROCKS

TEXTURE	Excess of light colored minerals						Excess of dark colored minerals		
	Feldspar orthoclase		Feldspar		Plagioclase		No feldspar		
	Mica [or and] hornblende [and] augite		Mica [or and] hornblende		with pyroxene		augite		augite [or and] hornblende [and] mica
	+quartz	−quartz	+quartz	−quartz	+olivine	−olivine	+olivine	−olivine	
Glassy	obsidian, perlite, pumice, pitchstone						scorias, trachylyte, basalt-obsidian		
Dense	rhyolite	trachite	dacite (felsite)	andesite (felsite)	basalt				
Porphyritic	rhyolite-porphyry	trachite-porphyry	dacite-porphyry	andesite-porphyry	basalt-porphyry				augitite-porphyry
Granitoid	granite	syenite	quartz-diorite	diorite	olivine-gabbro	gabbro	peridotite	pyroxenite	augitite or hornblendite
Fragmental	rhyolite, tuff or breccia	trachite, tuff or breccia	Dacite, tuff or breccia	andesite tuff or breccia	Basalt tuffs and breccias				

ture is present. If glassy, the color, luster and type of construction will place it. If the rock is crystalline, first decide whether feldspar is present, and if present, what type: then determine the dark mineral, and lastly whether quartz or olivine is present. In dense rocks the presence of quartz may be determined by trying the hardness, for none of the other constituents of igneous rocks have so great hardness. For example, if it is found that a rock is composed of orthoclase, hornblende and quartz, and the texture is granitoid, it is granite: or if the rock is plagioclase feldspar and pyroxene of any sort, it is gabbro, etc.

Granite
Pl. 53

The combination of orthoclase feldspar (or microcline), quartz, and either mica, hornblende or augite is termed granite, if the texture is coarse enough so the individual minerals can be recognized with the unaided eye. The rock is light-colored because the feldspar and quartz dominate. Accessory minerals may be present such as apatite, zircon, beryl or magnetite. Varieties of granite are distinguished according to the dark mineral present. When this is muscovite, it is a *muscovite-granite;* when it is biotite, a *biotite-granite;* if it is hornblende, a *hornblende-granite;* etc. The size of crystals in granite varies widely. When they are as small as $\frac{1}{12}$ of an inch in diameter, it is termed fine grained; from $\frac{1}{12}$ to $\frac{1}{4}$ of an inch, it is medium-grained; when larger, it is coarse-grained. In some cases the crystals may be over a foot in diameter which is known as *giant granite.*

Originally granite was a great mass of molten magma, which has cooled very slowly, having been intruded or thrust up in great stocks or batholiths beneath overlying rocks, which acted as a blanket to prevent rapid cooling. These overlying rocks, in their turn, have been acted upon by the heat and metamorphosed. Granite is particularly likely to have been formed under mountain folds; so that, after the mountains have been more or less completely eroded away, the great masses of granite have come to the surface to mark the axes of the ranges; and even after the mountains have been wholly worn away, the granite remains to mark the sites on which they stood.

In the granite mass itself, there are often veins and dykes, which probably resulted from the shrinkage of the cooling granite, and they are filled with a different and usually coarser granite known as **pegmatite.** This pegmatite formed from the residual magmatic material, so that as some of the elements had already crystallized out, the granite in these dikes is of different composition. The extreme coarseness of these pegmatites seems to be due to the character of the mineralizing agents left in the dikes. In some of these pegmatites the feldspar and quartz are so intergrown, that when broken along the cleavage surface of the feldspar, the quartz appears like cuneiform characters, and this variety has been given the name *graphic granite* (See Plate 53).

When granite is exposed to weathering, the feldspar is the first mineral to be decomposed, altering eventually into carbonates, quartz and kaolin. The dark minerals are only slightly less susceptible and they break down into carbonates, iron oxides and kaolin. The original quartz remains unchanged. Of these products the carbonates, some of the iron oxide and a little of the quartz are carried away in solution. The kaolin and some of the iron oxide is in fine particles and they are carried by the water until it comes to the lakes or the sea. The quartz is left in coarser grains, which are more slowly transported, and deposited in coarser or finer sand and gravel beds.

Granites are widely used for building stone, because they can be worked readily in all directions, and have great strength and beauty. The color depends largely on the color of the feldspar, which may be white or pink, in which case the granite will be gray to pink.

Granites occur throughout New England, the Piedmont Plateau, the Lake Superior Region, the Black Hills, Rocky Mountains, Sierra Nevada, etc.

Syenite
Pl. 54
The combination of orthoclase and either mica, hornblende, or augite is syenite, the texture being coarse enough so that the individual minerals can be distinguished by the unaided eye. It differs from granite in the absence of quartz. Syenite is a light-colored rock with the feldspar predominating. Minerals like apatite, zircon, or magnetite may occur in it, as accessory minerals. The foregoing would be an ideal syenite, but usually there is some plagioclase feldspar also

present. If this occurs in such quantities as to nearly equal the orthoclase feldspar, the rock is termed a *monzonite;* if it predominates, the rock becomes a diorite. The presence of quartz would make this rock into a granite. Such a compound rock has its type form, and when the proportions of the component minerals are changed, it grades into other types.

Like the granite, syenite is an intrusive rock, which occurs in stocks and batholiths along the axes of present or past mountain ranges. The original magma welled up under the mountain folds, where it cooled slowly, metamorphosing the adjacent rocks. Like granite it has only been exposed after a long period of erosion has removed the overlying layers of rock.

Syenites are not as abundant as granites, but they occur in the White Mountains, near Little Rock, Ark., in Custer Co., Colo., etc.

Quartz-Diorite The combination of plagioclase feldspar, quartz and either mica or hornblende makes quartz-diorite, sometimes called *tonalite.* The above would be the typical quartz-diorite, but there is usually some orthoclase present, which if it equals the plagioclase feldspar in amount makes this into a monzonite; or if it dominates, it makes the rock a granite. Quartz-diorite is darker colored than the two preceding rocks, the dark minerals being about as abundant as the light-colored ones, such as feldspar and quartz. For this reason the weight is also somewhat greater.

Like the others this is an intrusive rock, occurring in stocks and batholiths, and indicative of great molten masses thrust up under mountain folds, and only exposed after the overlying rocks have been weathered away. It is by no means an abundant type of rock, but occurs at Belchertown, Mass., Peekskill, N. Y., in the Yellowstone Park, etc.

Diorite
Plagioclase feldspar with hornblende or mica, or with both, is known as diorite. It is distinguished from quartz-diorite by the absence of quartz. There is generally some augite in it, but if this should be equal to, or exceed the hornblende, the rock is then a gabbro. There may also be a small amount of orthoclase present, without taking this rock out of the diorite class, but if the orthoclase feldspar becomes dominant, then the rock is a syenite. Thus there is gradation into other groups in all directions. Apatite, magnetite, zircon, and titanite often occur in small quantities as accessory minerals. Generally the hornblende is in excess of the feldspar, so that the rock is a dark-colored one.

Diorites occur in much the same manner as granites, being in stocks, batholiths or dykes, and are often associated with granites and gabbros. They are great intruded masses, associated with mountain making, and like the preceding rocks, cooled far below the surface, and have been exposed only after great thicknesses of overlying rocks have been weathered away.

Peekskill, N. Y., the Sudbury nickel district in Canada, Mt. Davidson above the Comstock

Lode in Nevada, etc., are typical localities for finding diorite.

Olivine-Gabbro The combination of plagioclase feldspar with augite (or any of the pyroxenes) and olivine makes olivine-gabbro. The feldspar is usually one of those with considerable calcium in it, like labradorite; and as the dark minerals predominate, the rock is dark-colored. It is an intrusive rock, usually in dykes or stocks, where it solidified far below the surface, and was only exposed after the overlying rocks were weathered off. It is by no means an abundant type of rock, but is found in the Lake Superior Region, and near Birch Lake, Minn.

Gabbro Pl. 54 Plagioclase feldspar with any one of the pyroxenes, most commonly augite, is gabbro. There is a wide range in the relative proportions of the two minerals making gabbro. At one extreme are rocks made entirely, or almost entirely, of plagioclase feldspar, which are known as **anorthosites,** and occur in parts of the higher mountains of the Adirondacks like Mt. Marcy, in several places in eastern Canada, etc. Then there are the typical gabbros where the feldspar and augite are more or less equally represented. At the other extreme come those gabbros in which the pyroxene predominates, in the most marked cases the feldspar being entirely lacking, and the rock being termed a pyroxenite. When the pyroxene of a gabbro is either enstatite or hyposthene (usually the latter) the gabbro is often called **norite**. Magnetite, biotite, and hornblende may occur in small quantities as accessory minerals.

Gabbro is a common intrusive rock, occurring in stocks, batholiths, and dikes, and often varies considerably in different parts of the mass. Like granite the mass solidified far below the surface, under some mountain fold, and has only been exposed as the result of weathering away the layers of overlying rock. Gabbros appear much like diorites, but are distinguished by the fact that the dark mineral is one of the pyroxenes, instead of an amphibole or a mica. They are widely distributed, being found in the White Mountains, near Peekskill, N. Y., Baltimore, Md., about Lake Superior, in Wyoming, the Rocky Mts., etc.

Peridotite A rock made up of olivine and augite (or any of the pyroxenes) is periodotite. As it contains no feldspar, and both augite and olivine are dark-green to black in color, these rocks are always dark green to black in color and of considerable weight. They are usually rather coarsely crystalline. Peridotite is usually associated with gabbro, making dikes which lead from the main gabbro mass. Less frequently it occurs independently, making up an intrusive mass. Hornblende and mica may be present in small quantities, as accessory minerals.

In general these are rather rare rocks, making dikes connected with stocks or batholiths of gabbro. Peridotite is found near Baltimore, Md., in Custer Co., Colo., in Kentucky, etc.

Pyroxenite   This represents the extreme among coarsely crystalline igneous rocks, a whole mass made up of one mineral, and that some one of the pyroxene group. If the mineral can be exactly determined, the rock may be still more definitely named. For instance if it is all augite, then the rock would be called augitite. Like the preceding rocks, pyroxenite is an intrusive rock, usually found in dikes, which are connected with gabbro, and it represents the segregation of one mineral out of the gabbro, and its solidification at one point. Hornblende, magnetite and pyrrhotite may be present as accessory minerals. This is not a common rock, but it illustrates the fact that all possible combinations do occur, if the circumstances have warranted it. It is found near Baltimore, Md., Webster, N. C., and in Montana.

Rhyolite   This is a combination of orthoclase feldspar, quartz, and either hornblende, mica or augite in which the crystals are of such small size that they can not be identified with the naked eye. In composition it corresponds to granite, but it is much finer in texture. It differs from trachite by having quartz while the latter has none. This can usually be determined by trying the hardness as none of the other minerals are as hard as 7. It is much harder to distinguish it from dacite which differs only in having plagioclase feldspar in place of the orthoclase, and only the microscope will enable one to make this distinction. Where the distinction cannot be made these light-colored lavas are often called **felsite.**

Rhyolite is usually an extrusive lava, occurring in sheets, but sometimes it is intrusive, occurring in sills, dikes, and laccoliths. In all these cases the lava has solidified so rapidly, that the crystals are tiny, and only the general effect of a crystalline structure is distinguishable. Rhyolites may occur with porphyritic structure, in which case the presence of the larger feldspar crystals will help to distinguish whether they are orthoclase or not, making the determination easier. The color of rhyolites is green, red or gray, always a decided light shade.

Rhyolites are abundant in the western states, as in the Black Hills, the Yellowstone Park, Colorado, Nevada, California, etc.

Trachite The combination of orthoclase feldspar with mica, hornblende or augite is termed trachite, if the texture is dense. It is usually an extrusive lava of light color (green, red or gray), and corresponds in composition to syenite. It can be distinguished from rhyolite by having no quartz, and so nothing to show a hardness above 5.5; but it is difficult to distinguish it from andesite, which differs only in having plagioclase feldspar in place of orthoclase. It sometimes occurs with a porphyritic structure, in which case the feldspar crystals are usually large enough to be distinguished.

Trachites are not abundant in America, but some are found in the Black Hills of South Dakato, in Custer Co., Colo., and in Montana.

Dacite The union of plagioclase feldspar, quartz, and either hornblende or mica is termed dacite, if the texture is dense. It is an extrusive lava, occurring mostly in sheets and dikes. It corresponds in composition to quartz-diorite. As the texture is dense it is difficult to distinguish dacite from rhyolite, for both have quartz and differ only in the character of the feldspar, so it is quite common to use the term felsite which does not distinguish between the two, and only states that the rock is dense, light-colored and extrusive. When, as often occurs, the texture is porphyritic, and the feldspars are the large crystals, then exact determination is fairly easy.

Dacites are rather common, occurring on McClelland Peak, Nev., in the Eureka district, Nev., on Lassen's Peak, Calif., Sepulchre Mt. in the Yellowstone Park, etc.

Andesite The union of plagioclase feldspar with mica, hornblende or augite makes andesite if the texture is dense. The lack of quartz, and so no mineral which has a hardness of over 5.5, makes it possible to distinguish andesite from dacite or rhyolite, but it is hard to distinguish this rock from trachite, which differs only on having orthoclase feldspar in place of plagioclase. When the texture is porphyritic and the feldspars are the large crystals, then it is easy to make the distinction. Andesite gets its name from being the characteristic lava of the Andes Mountains, and is the commonest of all the extruded, light-colored lavas, being the lava of hundreds of flows throughout the western United States.

The union of plagioclase feldspar and biotite is the commonest type. Plagioclase with hornblende or augite is less common, and, when they do occur, they are usually distinguished as *hornblende-andesite* or *augite-andesite*. Magnetite, apatite and zircon may be present as accessory minerals.

The lavas of Mt. Hood, Shasta, Rainier and others of the volcanic peaks of the Cascade Range, those at Eureka and Comstock in Nevada, in the Yellowstone National Park, and the porphyries of many peaks in Colorado, like the Henry Mts., etc., which are exposed laccolithic intrusions, are all andesites, as are many more.

Basalt The combination of plagioclase feldspar with olivine and augite (or any other pyroxene) makes a heavy, dark-colored, black to dark-brown rock which, if its texture is dense or porphyritic, is termed basalt. This usually has more or less magnetite in it as an accessory mineral, indeed the magnetite may be so abundant as to be a component part of t e rock. This magnetite makes trouble for anyone trying to use a compass on or about basalt rocks. These are extrusive or intrusive rocks and correspond in composition to gabbro.

Basalts are among the commonest of igneous rocks, and are popularly designated "*trap*," much used as a road ballast on account of its toughness, which is largely due to its dense texture. The coast of New England is seamed with dikes of basalt, and through the Adirondack and White Mountains there are a host of these dikes. The crests of such mountains, as the Holyoke Range, the Tom Range, the Talcott Mts., East and West Rocks at New Haven, etc., are all basalt sheets. The Palisades, First Wachung and Second Wachung Mountains of New Jersey are sills of basalt. The Lake Superior region is crisscrossed with basalt dikes. That greatest of all lava fields the Columbia Plateau, covering over 200,000 square miles on the Snake and Columbia Rivers in Oregon, Washington and Idaho, is all basalt. So it goes all down through Nevada, New Mexico and California.

Porphyry
Pl. 55
This is a term which properly refers to texture alone, indicating a lava, which has cooled in such a manner that one mineral has crystallized out of the magma first and developed to a larger size, while the mass of the material formed tiny crystals in which the larger ones are embedded. The large crystals are technically known as *phenocrysts*. The surrounding mass of tiny crystals is termed the *matrix*. This porphyritic structure is especially characteristic of lavas which have been extruded in large masses, and of intruded lavas in such places as sills and laccoliths.

The term porphyry today has the above precise meaning. It is a much abused word, and has had all sorts of meanings. In the past it was first used to refer to lavas in general, then it came to be applied to lavas which had been erupted before Tertiary times, that is to all ancient lava sheets. This idea soon proved incorrect, lavas being of the same composition whether ancient or recent. In the West the word is often colloquially used today to designate almost every kind of igneous rock occurring in sheets or dikes, if in any way connected with ore deposits.

When the composition of a rock with porphyritic textures can be determined, the name due to the composition is coupled with that due to texture, making such terms as *trachite-porphyry*, *basalt-porphyry*, etc.

Tuff   Tuff, a term not to be confused with tufa on page 215, is the name used to designate the finer fragmental ejecta of volcanic eruptions, which are also often referred to as "volcanic ash," but the word, ash, conveys the false impression that the rock is a remnant of something burned, and is therefore not a good term. When first ejected, tuff is loose material, but it is usually soon cemented to make a more or less firm mass of rock, for which the term, tuff, is still retained. In some cases, while still loose, it is carried by streams to a distance and deposited in more or less sorted and layered beds: and the finer tuff is often carried by the winds and laid down, at a considerable distance from its source, in so called "ash beds." In both these cases, sedimentary characteristics have been added to the tuff, and layering which is characteristic of sedimentary deposits, is present. These transported tuff beds are really sedimentary, but as there is little change in the material, they are referred to here and not again. These tuff beds are not at all uncommon in the sedimentary deposits of Tertiary age in the Rocky Mountain region. The coarser material of volcanic eruptions usually goes under the head of breccia.

Breccia This term is used to describe the coarse fragmental ejecta of volcanic eruptions. It is also used, in the section under sedimentary rocks, in a broad sense to include all angular unworn fragmental material, whether of igneous or sedimentary origin. For this reason, when dealing with igneous rocks, it is usual to designate the fragments according to their composition, making such terms as *trachite-breccia*, *rhyolite-breccia*, etc.

While still loose (and also even when cemented into beds of rock), it is customary to designate the smaller fragments, from the size of a grain of wheat up to an inch or two in diameter, as *lapalli;* the larger fragments, from two inches up to a foot or so in diameter, as *bombs;* and the largest masses, often tons in weight, as *volcanic blocks.*

Obsidian
Pl. 55 Lavas, which have cooled so quickly that crystals have not had time to form, have a glassy appearance, and are termed obsidian. If the color is dark, due to the presence of large amounts of those elements which make dark minerals, this lava is termed *basalt-obsidian*. Obsidian is

characterized by its glassy texture, a hardness around 6, and by breaking with a conchoidal fracture, so called because the surface is marked by a series of concentric ridges, something like the lines of growth on a shell. Obsidians vary greatly in color, but are usually red or green to black, and translucent on thin edges. While glassy, all the obsidians contain embryonic crystals, which appear like dust particles floating in the glassy matrix, or there may even be a few larger crystals present, which are often arranged in flow lines. Most all large masses of obsidian have streaks or layers of stony material in them where crystallization has set in, in a limited way.

Near the upper surface, obsidians usually have gas cavities scattered through them, and these may be small and few, or large and numerous. Indeed the cavities may be so numerous as to dominate and give the rock a frothy appearance. In this case, if the cavities are small and more or less uniform, the rock is called *pumice;* if they are larger it is *scoria*. If, as often happens when the lava is ancient and has been buried beneath other rocks, the cavities have been filled with some secondary mineral, then the lava is called an *amygdoloid*.

Obsidian is found in many localities, especially where there are recent volcanoes, the most famous places being the obsidian cliffs in the Yellowstone Park, those near Mono Lake in California, and many other localities in the Rocky Mountains, the Sierra Nevadas, and the Cascade Mountains.

Pitchstone   This is very like obsidian in appearance, but differs in that the glassy material contains from five to ten per cent of water in its composition, the most obvious effect of which is to make the luster resinous, instead of vitreous, as is characteristic of obsidian. The colors are commonly red, green or brown. Pitchstone is associated with recent volcanoes, and some fine specimens have come from Silver Cliffs, Colo., and various parts of New Mexico and Nevada.

Perlite   *pearlstone*   Perlite is a glassy lava, containing two to four per cent of water, which, on cooling, has cracked into numerous rounded masses, with a concentric structure, reminding one of the layers of an onion.

Scoria   While lava is cooling, there is a constant escape of gases, mostly steam, and as these rise through the molten mass they make cavities, near the upper surface, that portion on top often becoming frothy. If this solidifies quickly so that the gas cavities are preserved it is scoria. When the gas cavities are small and uniformly distributed, the rock is called pumice, and often used as a scouring agent. When the cavities are large and irregular the term scoria is generally used. Molten lavas may form various structures, according to the conditions under which they cool, dripping through cracks or from the roof of caves, which often form where the molten lava escapes from a hardened shell, and making stalactites, stalagmites, etc. The very thin lava of the Hawaiian volcanoes may even be blown by the wind into fine threads, known as "Peleé's hair."

The presence of the gas cavities is so characteristic of the upper surface of lavas which have been extruded; that, where one is dealing with older lavas, now buried beneath other rocks, this fact helps to determine whether the mass is a sheet, rather than a sill; for, in the case of the sill, the lava was forced between layers of sedimentary rocks, and the burden of the overlying rocks did not permit the escape of steam and therefore the upper surface of sills does not have the scoriaceous structure.

Amygdoloid
Pl. 56

When the upper surface of a lava is filled with steam holes, and this lava has been buried beneath other rocks, the seeping waters slowly bring such minerals as quartz, calcite and zeolites and fill the cavities. Such a rock is known as an amygdoloid. It is often confused with porphyry; but, if examined closely, it will be seen that the outlines of the gas cavities are rounded, while the outlines of a crystal, like a phenocryst, are always angular. This will be clear if the amygdoloid on Plate 56 is compared with the porphyry on Plate 55.

THE SEDIMENTARY ROCKS

To this class belong all those rocks which have been laid down by water or wind, or are the results of organic depositions. They include loose material like sand or clay, and also the same materials, when cemented into more or less solid rocks, like sandstone or shale. So long as the material has not been altered from what it was when laid down, the rock is termed sedimentary.

In general the material of which these rocks are composed comes from the weathering and disintegration of other rocks. This does not apply to the organic deposits, for each type of which there is a peculiar mode of formation. To illustrate the typical formation of sedimentary rocks, we may look at the fate of a granite when exposed. At once the surface is attacked by changes of temperature, frost and rain. The various minerals of the granite expand and contract with every change of temperature, but each component mineral has a different coefficient of expansion under heat, so that minute cracks are quickly formed between the minerals. Water gets into these cracks and begins to dissolve the minerals. Feldspar is the most easily attacked, part of it being dissolved and carried away, a small part changing to quartz, and by far the largest part changing to kaolin. The dark mineral is also attacked and partly dissolved, and partly changed to kaolin and iron oxides. The quartz resists solution almost completely. Of these products the kaolin and iron oxides are carried far away and deposited in still water. The quartz and perhaps some of the dark mineral are heavier and carried more slowly, being deposited as sand. This happens to granite everywhere, but in the regions where there is frost the action is greatly hastened; for water gets into the cracks and expands every time it freezes and thus widens the cracks rapidly, which greatly facilitates the entrance and movement of water in the rock. In a similar way any original rock will be disintegrated, and the residue, after the soluble part has been carried away, becomes sand or clay or mud.

Particles of quartz, kaolin, and lime, separately, or mixed, loose or more or less cemented, with accompanying impurities, make up the great bulk of the sedimentary rocks. They are usually arranged in layers, of varying thickness, as they were laid down by water or the wind. In the same way layered accumulations which are either products of plants or animals, or parts of the plants or animals, are considered sedimentary, as for instance, coal, chalk, petroleum, etc.

A CLASSIFICATION OF SEDIMENTARY ROCKS

Inorganic origin:

1. Coarse fragmentary material resulting from weathering talus
2. The same fragmentary material cemented breccia
3. Unsorted material resulting from rock weathering soil
4. Coarse fragments rounded by the action of water and wind gravel
5. The same material cemented conglomerate

6. Finer material deposited by
     water or wind   sand
7. The same material cemented   sandstone
8. The finest material, mostly
     kaolin, deposited by water   clay
9. The finest material, deposited
     by wind   loess
10. The same material cemented   shale
11. Fine particles of lime, pure
      or impure   marl
12. The same material cemented   limestone
13. Unassorted material left by
      the glacial ice   till
14. The same material cemented   tillite

Organic Origin:

15. Limes made from shells, etc.—coquina, chalk,
      coral rock, etc.
16. Silica from the shells of plants, etc.,—diato-
      maceous earth, etc.
17. Carbon from plants—peat, lignite, coal, etc.
18. Hydrocarbons from animals—petroleum, as-
      phalt, amber, etc.
19. Phosphates from animals—guano, phos-
      phate rock, etc.

Talus   Where weathering is very active,
                especially on or below steep moun-
tain slopes, a mass of loose, angular fragments
accumulates. This material is termed talus, a
term which refers only to the physical character
of the material, and not at all to its composition.
If weathering continues these fragments will be

further broken up into one of the finer grained rocks, which the water can carry away and deposit elsewhere. There is little or no layering in talus. If the talus is not carried away but is cemented where it was formed, the resulting mass is termed breccia, but this is not very commonly the case.

**Breccia
Pl. 58**

The term breccia is used to cover all those rocks which are composed of angular fragments, of any composition, and above sand in size, when they are cemented into a solid mass, by any sort of cementing agent. Here the term is used in its broad sense, as compared with the way it was used under igneous rocks.

Breccias may result from the cementing of talus, but more often the breaking up of the material into angular fragments was due to other causes, such as crushing along a fault plane, or in the movements involved in mountain making. In such cases the breccia is of limited extent, but may occur repeatedly in the same neighborhood. Limestone, which has been crushed and then recemented, often makes a rock which takes a good polish and is used in several localities as an ornamental stone in place of marble, in fact often goes in trade circles under the name of "marble." The breccia figured on Plate 58 is such a limestone.

Soil

Over most of the earth's surface there is a covering of rock waste, the product of weathering, some of which is

unassorted, and some of it sorted by water or
wind. This is all termed soil. It is an ever-
moving cover resulting from the decomposition
of the underlying rocks, to which have been
added in places layers of rock waste brought
from afar by the streams. Some soils are rock
waste which had been carried clear to the ocean
and deposited on the floor of the sea, and is now
above sea level, because the floor of the sea
has been elevated. Inasmuch as the underlying rocks vary in composition, and as there are
areas of transported material, it is clear that
the composition of soils must vary from place to
place, both as to composition and texture.

Soils range from the finest, composed mostly
of clay, to coarse ones, composed of sand, gravel
or even boulders. Clay, the finest grained soil,
is composed of particles only about $\frac{1}{1000}$th of a
millimeter in diameter, of which it would take
720,000 billion particles to make a gram's weight.
Ordinary soils however have about 2 to 5 million
particles to the gram.

The average specific gravity of soil with the
usual amount of humus in it is from 2.55 to 2.75.
In this case however the specific gravity is of
less importance than is the volume weight. A
cubic foot of water weighs $62\frac{1}{2}$ pounds, that of
soil from 75 to 80 pounds, the extremes being
30 lb. for peaty soil and 110 lb. for calcareous
sand. The terms "heavy" and "light," used
in agriculture do not refer to the volume weight,
for clay which is actually relatively light (70–75
lb. per cubic foot) is classed as a "heavy" soil;
while sand, of much greater actual weight, is

classed as a "light" soil. These terms as used in agriculture refer to the ease with which the soils are worked, and to their penetrability by plant roots.

Soil is usually divided into an upper darker-colored layer, termed loam, and into a lower, lighter-colored layer, termed subsoil. The presence of humus, resulting from the decomposition of plant and animal remains is the factor which darkens the color and distinguishes the loam; so that loam is a complex of inorganic rock particles plus more or less humus, colloid compounds, bacteria, living plants and animals. The subsoil is mainly rock particles. The distinctions between these two layers break down in arid soils, and often also in swampy regions.

It is this layer of soil on which the water of every rain and flood works, picking part of it up and carrying it along, step by step, to the sea. Though the amount moved on any one day is small, the sum of all the soil transported is enormous, a large river carrying annual incredible amounts. For instance the Mississippi annually deposits in the Gulf of Mexico 476,900,-000 metric tons (2204 lb. to the metric ton), of which about a third is in solution. At this rate it takes about 7000 to 9000 years to remove a foot from over the whole drainage basin. This is considerably slower than is the case of some other rivers. While on the one hand soil is being continuously carried away from the surface, on the other hand it is being constantly renewed from below, by the weathering action of water, air and temperature.

Gravel Gravel is a mass of loose fragments of rock, which have been
rounded by water and deposited with little or no
sorting, so that larger and smaller pebbles and
sand all occur together. It is the deposit laid
down by comparatively fast water in inland lakes
or along the storm-beaten shores of the sea.
Where a swift stream enters quiet water, as
where it empties into a lake, there it quickly
drops its coarse material as gravel, usually thus
building a delta. Gravel also occurs in stream
beds, where for any reason the rate of flow is
checked. During the recent glacial period, the
ice sheet brought down great masses of unsorted
material, which was deposited as till, or in
moraines. Much of this was then picked up by
the running water and moved longer or shorter
distances, so that, all over the glaciated country
of the northern and eastern United States, there
are unusually large numbers of gravel deposits.
Gravels are all water laid, and usually show more
or less clearly the bedded or stratified structure.

The size of the component pebbles of gravel
ranges from great boulders to fine sand, and the
finer gravels grade into the coarser sands, the line
between gravel and sand being drawn at about
the size of a pea, the coarser being gravel, the
finer sand.

Gravel is widely used as ballast for railroads
and in making highways, because of its tendence
to pack well, while the hard pebbles resist wear.
It is also widely used in concrete work, bonding
in well with the cement, and making it go from
three to five times as far.

Conglomerate, Pl. 58

Conglomerates are composed of rounded pebbles and sand of varying sizes, cemented together into a solid rock. The pebbles may run up to boulders in size, but they have all been more or less rounded by water, and transported some distance. The pebbles may all be of the same composition, or may represent a variety of rocks. When the pebbles are all, or most all, of one sort the resulting conglomerate is termed a *quartz conglomerate*, a *limestone-conglomerate*, a *gneiss-conglomerate*, etc. So too the cementing material varies in kind, silica, calcite and iron oxide being the commonest. The color will depend on both the component pebbles and the cement, sometimes one dominating, sometimes the other. There are some of the quartz- and limestone-conglomerates which can be cut and polished to make very handsome stone.

Conglomerates represent consolidated gravels, and always indicate an aqueous origin, quite often the delta of an ancient stream, or the invasion of the sea over the land; so they have become of importance to geologists in interpreting past events.

Sand

Sand is a mass of small rock particles, from the size of a pea down to $\frac{1}{500}$ of an inch in diameter. The material may be any sort of rock, or a mixture of two or more kinds. Sand may be the result of the disintegration of older rocks at the point where it is now found, in which case the grains have the shapes they had in the original rock; but more often the sand grains have been transported greater or lesser distances, and in the process have been more or less rounded.

Those sands, which lie where they were formed are called *residual*, and such sand is usually composed of a mixture of angular grains, some harder and others softer, such as quartz, feldspar, mica and hornblende, all mixed together. Where the sand has been transported, only the more resistant minerals have remained, such as quartz, magnetite, cassiderite, etc.; with which there are at times rarer minerals, such as gold, platinum, garnets or topaz. Such sands are known as *gold-bearing*, *topaz-bearing*, etc.

The sands from different localities differ greatly. The streams gather the rock particles, and sort them according to the size, which the water flowing at any given rate can carry. When the water is slowed down, it drops all the particles above the size which the new rate of speed can handle. The grains of sand from the bed of a stream are usually more or less angular. The further they are carried, the more they are knocked together and rounded; so that after being carried to the sea, and then thrown up on the beaches, they have been well rounded, especially the larger grains. As the air is less viscid than the water, sand which is transported by the wind, is even more rounded; so that desert sands show the most complete rounding, indeed are even polished; and this is true even of the smaller grains. It is the wind-blown, or desert sands, which flow so evenly in an hourglass. Between the angular residual sands and the polished desert sands, there are of course all grades. Glacial sands are angular or "sharp" almost to the degree characteristic of residual sands; and lake-shore sands are between river sands and sea sands in the degree of rounding.

Sands made of particles of lime, *calcareous sands,* are less resistant to wear than are those of quartz. In regions where the water is "soft" (free from lime), they do not last long, as they are dissolved; but in a limestone region where the water is "hard" (saturated with lime), the grains are not so quickly dissolved and may accumulate into beds of great thickness, as in Florida. Along some shores of the ocean, there occur "green sands," which are ordinary quartz sands mixed with the dark green mineral glauco nite, which is a potassium iron silicate, forming on the ocean bottom as a result of the action of decaying animal matter on iron-bearing clays and potassium-bearing silicates, like feldspar. This is particularly characteristic of some of the sands along the coast of New Jersey.

In places, especially in the beds of rivers, there occur "quicksands." This is a deposit of fine sand, mixed with a considerable amount of clay, and saturated with water; so that it will not support the weight of a man or an animal. Much that goes under the name of quicksand is a fluid mud, covered with a thin layer of sand.

Sand is used for a wide variety of commercial purposes, and under these conditions gets various trade names; for instance "glass sand" is a pure, colorless to white, quartz sand, which is used as one of the components in making glass. It must be free from impurities, as these color the glass, and much of the sand used for this purpose is quartz, crushed to a fine sand-like condition. "Moulding sand" is a rather fine-grained quartz sand, with a small but very definite admixture of clay, and this is used to make the moulds for castings in foundries. "Polishing sand" is one composed of angular fragments of quartz, usually from stream beds or glacial deposits, or even crushed quartz, and is used for cutting and polishing marble, for sandpaper, and for polishing wood and softer stones. There are many other special uses, like building, ballast, filters, furnaces, etc., in which quartz sand is used, being screened if necessary to get the right sizes.

Sandstone When sand of any sort is cemented so as to make a solid rock, it is termed sandstone, which varies widely according to the size, color and composition of the grains, and also with the sort and amount of the cement. When the size of the grains is larger than that of a pea, sandstone grades into conglomerate; when smaller than $\frac{1}{500}$th of an inch, especially if mixed with clay, it grades into shale. There are all grades of firmness, due to the amount and kind of cement, ranging from those which have little or no cement, but are compact as a result of the pressure of the overlying rocks, to those in which the cement has filled all the pore spaces. In general there is a considerable amount of space between the grains of sand; so that a sandstone will absorb large amounts of water, up to 25% of its bulk.

In moist climates where it freezes, this makes many sandstones unsuitable for use as building stones, as they are likely to spale, or chip off, as is seen in the "brown stone" so much used in New York City.

Sandstones are usually bedded rocks and are relatively easy to quarry, and most of them are not so firmly cemented, but that they can be readily worked or cut into shape by the stone cutter; and so, certain sandstones are very popular for building stone or for trimming on buildings, where they are not too much exposed to the weather.

Sandstone gets a variety of names according to the cement.

Siliceous sandstone is cemented with silica and usually very hard.

Calcareous sandstone is cemented with lime and usually rather soft.

Ferruginous sandstone is cemented with one of the iron oxides.

Argillaceous sandstone is held together with clay impurities, and is usually both soft and of undesirable color.

According to their composition there is also a number of varieties.

Arkose is a sandstone composed of quartz and feldspar grains, usually derived from the disintegration of granite and not transported far.

Graywacke is a sandstone composed of quartz, feldspar, and some other mineral, like hornblende-augite, etc., also derived from the disintegration of granites and not transported far.

Grit is a term applied to a coarse sandstone.

composed of angular quartz fragments, and used to a considerable extent for millstones.

Flagstone is a thin bedded sandstone, often with mica, which splits easily and uniformly along the bedding planes; so that it can be quarried in large slabs. It was widely used for sidewalks before the advent of concrete.

Freestone is a thick-bedded sandstone, not over hard, so called, because it can be worked freely and equally well in all directions.

Clay   Clay is a term used to describe a mass of fine particles, the most prominent property of which is plasticity when wet. Clays range from masses of pure kaolin to masses of kaolin and related minerals mixed with as much as 60% of impurities, which may be sand, lime, iron oxides, etc. The particles of a fine clay range around $\frac{1}{1000}$ of a millimeter in diameter, while the impurities may be, and usually are, of larger size, up to the size of sand grains.

All clays are of secondary origin, the result of weathering, especially of feldspars, though clays may also result from the weathering of serpentines, gabbros, etc. In some cases after the weathering of feldspar or limestones, the clay may remain just where it was formed, as a residual deposit; but, being so fine-grained, it is usually transported by rain water or by the wind and deposited somewhere else as a sedimentary bed. The quiet waters of a lake are favorable places for such deposits, and many clay beds represent former lake bottoms. Impure clays are often laid down on the flood plains of sluggish streams. In fresh water the settling of the clay is a very slow process, requiring days, or when very fine, weeks, before the water wholly clears. In salt water, however, the clay sort of coagulates, the particles gathering together in tiny balls, which settle rapidly, so that the water is soon clear.

According to their mode of origin clays are classified as residual, sedimentary, marine, swamp, lake, flood-plain, eolian, etc. But when their uses are considered a very different classification is made, based mostly on their composition, and we speak of China clays or kaolins, fire or refractory clays, paving-brick clays, sewer-pipe, stone-ware, brick, gumbo and slip clays.

The **kaolin** or **china clays** are residual clays, usually resulting from the decomposition of pegmatite dikes. They must be white when burned, free from iron oxides, and fairly plastic. A good deal of china clay is made by crushing feldspar.

Ball clays are sedimentary clays which remain white when burned, are usually very plastic, and free from iron oxides. They are mostly used in the making of various sorts of china.

Fire clays may or may not have iron oxides in them, but they must be free or nearly free from fluxing materials, such as lime, magnesia and the alkalies (sodium and potassium compounds). They may be more or less plastic, the essential quality being their ability to withstand high temperatures without fusing. Silica (as sand) tends to diminish the refractory quality; so that a clay otherwise suitable, if it has sand in it, becomes at best a second grade fire clay. In coal mining sections it is customary to term those beds of clay either above or below the coal, "fire clay"; but this is an unfortunate designation, for though some of them are true fire clays, the most of them are not.

Stone-ware clays are those with considerable sand and up to five per cent of fluxing materials. They must be plastic enough to be readily worked, and then burn to a dense body at comparatively low temperatures.

Sewer-pipe clays must be plastic, and carry a considerable amount of fluxing material, as the surface of the pipe is expected to vitrify in the burning.

Brick clays are low grade clays and vary greatly in composition. The main requisites are that they mould easily and bake hard at relatively low temperatures with as little warping and cracking as possible. As most clays shrink both in the air drying and in the baking, sand is added when the clay is being mixed. The color is mostly due to the presence of iron impurities. If there are iron oxides and little or no lime, the brick bakes to a red color, but if there is an excess of lime over the iron oxides, it bakes to a cream or buff color, which on vitrifying turns green.

Paving-brick clays range from surface clays, to semirefractory clays, shale being often used. The essential component is enough fluxing material, so that the bricks shall begin to vitrify, or fuse, at not too high temperatures.

Slip clays are those with a high percentage of fluxing material; so that, when baked at moderate temperatures, the surface fuses into a glassy brown or green glaze.

Adobe is an impure calcareous clay, widely used in the western United States for making sun-dried bricks.

Gumbo is a term applied to fine-grained plastic clays which shrink too much in the burning to be useful in manufactures. They can be burned to make an excellent ballast for railroads and highways. They are especially abundant in the Middle Western States.

Loess   This is the name given to a fine grained homogeneous clay-like material, which is a mixture of clay, fine angular fragments of sand, flakes of mica and more or less calcareous matter. It is usually without stratification, and cleaves vertically, so that, when eroded, it forms steep cliffs. Loess covers great areas in the Mississippi Valley, in the Rhine Valley, and in North Central China. By some it is thought to be an accumulation of dust in those regions where the prevailing winds were of diminished velocity and where the grass or other vegetation has served to catch and hold the material; by others it is thought of as a river and lake deposit; and by still others it is thought to be due to the combination of the two modes, wind and flood. The writer inclines to the first view expressed.

**Shale
Pl. 59**   When pure or impure clays, or loess, are consolidated, they are all grouped under the name shale. It usually possesses a layered or stratified structure,

which makes it possible to split it into thin
layers. Of all the sedimentary rocks shale is the
commonest, and it may occur in all the places
where clay could occur, but the most widely
distributed shale is that which made the sea
bottom of former times and is more or less calcareous, like the piece on Plate 59, in which bits
of shells are still visible. Shale has the same
wide variation in composition as has clay, the
various types being designated according to the
impurity which is present, as:

argillaceous shale, made mostly of clay,

arenaceous shale, shale with more or less sand
as an impurity,

calcareous shale, or one with more or less lime
as an impurity,

ferruginous shale, or one with iron compounds
as impurities,

bituminous shale, or one colored black by the
presence of organic matter, remains of either
plants or animals.

While of no value as building material, shale
may be ground or crushed, and used as a substitute for any corresponding clay, and thus many
manufacturers use shale in making fire-clay
products, bricks, tile, etc.

Marl Where limestones or shells of any
sort have been pulverized, and
mixed with more or less impurities, especially
clay, the resulting unconsolidated mass is known
as marl. It is usually associated with marine
formations, and is the finer débris which has
settled on the ocean bottom well out from shore,

that is out beyond the sandy and mud deposits. Finding it therefore usually indicates a sea bottom recently elevated. It is very characteristic of the southern coastal states, from Maryland all along to Texas.

Limestone   Any mass of marl, or aggregate of calcareous shells, corals, etc., which has become consolidated is known as limestone. It may, and usually does, have a wide range of impurities, chief of which are clay, sand, iron oxides, and bituminous matter, like plant or animal remains. Pure limestone is white, but due to impurities it ranges through grays, greens, browns, to black, and even red, but this last is rarer. It is easily identified by the presence of calcium carbonate, which effervesces in hydrochloric acid. It most often represents deposits in fairly deep water on ocean bottoms of the past, but there is also a wide range of limestones which were formed in fresh water.

Limestone is often burned at temperatures just above 900° C, at which point carbon dioxide goes off as a gas, and leaves calcium oxide, or lime. When this is mixed with water it makes calcium hydroxide, or slaked lime, which is mixed with sand to give it body, and is used as mortar. When exposed to the air, the slaked lime gives up water, and takes back from the air carbon dioxide, and again becomes calcium carbonate with its original hardness. Limestone is also used as one of the elements in all cements. It is also considerably used as a building stone, which, however, suffers in moist climates from the solution of its lime by rains, but has stood up very well in dry climates.

The varieties of limestone are mostly distinguished according to their mode of origin, some of them being as follows.

Bog Lime is a white calcareous powdery deposit on the bottom of ponds in limestone regions, a deposit precipitated from solution by the action of the plants inhabiting the ponds.

Coquina (Plate 59) is the rock formed by the rather loose consolidation of shells and shell fragments. It is particularly characteristic of tropical regions, and is very abundant near St. Augustine, Fla., in which region it was, and still is, cut into blocks and used for building stone. In that mild climate it has stood very well.

Chalk (Plate 60) is a soft fine-grained limestone, formed in the ocean by the accumulation of myriads of the tiny shells of Foramenifera, which are single celled animals, living either a floating life near the surface of the sea, or a creeping life on the bottom. Chalk is composed mostly of the shells of floating Foramenifera, which when the animals died, settled to the bottom and there accumulated, mostly at depths of 600 feet or more. When the mass of unconsolidated shells is dredged up from depths of 50 to 2000 fathoms, it is known as *Foramenifera ooze*. Chalk beds are then indications of an uplifted sea bottom. When consolidated, if pure or nearly so, it makes a white chalk, and the beds may be of considerable thickness, as is the case of the famous cliffs near Dover on either side of the English Channel. One of Huxley'-

most famous lectures is the one on chalk, found in his *Essays and Lay Sermons*.

Coral Rock is made by the cementation of fragments of corals. The binding material, as in most stones, is lime; and this sort of rock is associated with coral reefs of either the past or the present. One of the best illustrations of this being the "Dolomite Mountains" in Tyrol. Coral rock, like coquina, has been cut into blocks and used as building stone, as in Bermuda.

Encrinal Limestone (Plate 60) is a rock made by the cementation of fragments of the skeleton of crinoids. These animals belong to the group, echinoderms, and are now extinct except for a few so called "sea-lilies." They were animals with a central mouth surrounded by long, jointed, flexible arms in multiples of five, and below this a small body inclosed in calcareous plates, all at the top of a long jointed stem. They lived in the sea and in the earlier geological times must have been very abundant; for their remains are so common in places as to make whole layers of limestone.

Hydraulic Limestone is a fine-grained, compact, yellowish limestone with from 13 to 17 % of sand, and some clay; which, when it is burned at a temperature a little higher than that used in burning lime, makes a product, that, while not as strong as Portland cement, still like it sets under water.

Lithographic Limestone is a very fine-grained compact, limestone with clay impurities, the finest of the grain making it usable for making the stone plates used in lithographic printing.

On slabs of this limestone figures are drawn in reverse with a special crayon. Then the slab is treated with acid, those parts which are not protected by the drawing being etched away, while the points protected by the drawing remain in low relief. From this slab figures can then be printed.

Travertine is a general name, applied to calcareous deposits from fresh water lakes or streams, and has been precipitated either as a result of cooling or evaporation. Some travertines are porous, while others are dense; some are white, while others are colored, often beautifully, by impurities in the water.

Porous deposits of travertine, when made on grass or other like substances, are known as tufa or *calc sinter.* Such masses are common around Caledonia, N. Y., Mammoth Hot Springs in the Yellowstone Park, etc.

Onyx marble is a dense travertine, usually formed as a result of the deposition of lime from the water of springs. It is often banded, due to the presence of impurities in the water at one time, and their absence at other times.

Till   Till is an unconsolidated mass of boulders, pebbles, sand and fine clay, the unsorted material left behind by glaciers when they melted. The boulders and pebbles, while they show some wear, are not rounded like those that have been transported by streams, but have a more or less angular shape; and some of them are polished or striated on one side, where, while frozen in the ice, they were rubbed along the bottom.

One of the most recent geological events in America was the extension of the ice sheet, now covering Greenland, down over north and northeastern North America, until it extended as far south as northern New Jersey, the Ohio River and the Missouri River, and as far west as the Rocky Mountains, but not over the Great Basin, the Cascade Ranges or Alaska. This great mass of ice, thousands of feet thick moved from two centers, one either side of Hudson Bay, scraping up the loose soil, and grinding off the exposed surfaces of the underlying rock. All this material it carried southward, until the melting along its lower margin equaled the rate at which it advanced. When the melting was faster than the advance the glacial sheet retreated. At the southern limit of the advance this débris was dropped, either making long ridges (moraines) or while the ice was retreating, thicker or thinner sheets. This deposited débris is till.

The soil, and especially the subsoil, in all the regions formerly covered by the ice sheet, is made up very largely of this till; which, where it is undisturbed is often called "hard pan." When till is mixed with humus it becomes loam. This mixture of material, varying all the way from the fine powdered products of the ice grinding to the great boulder it picked up and carried south, is characteristic of this or any other glaciated country. When this section of country was settled, the boulders and stone were a hindrance to cultivation, and were picked up and piled into stone walls, which are one of the first features to strike the eye.

Tillite   When till is consolidated into solid rock, it is known as tillite. In several cases it has been found buried far beneath the more recent sedimentary rocks; testifying that there were other glacial periods beside the last one which furnished the till.

THE COAL SERIES

Disregarding minor constituents, the plants are largely made up of cellulose, which is a combination of carbon, hydrogen, and oxygen, $(C_6H_{10}O_5)$. If this is heated in the air, where there is plenty of oxygen, it disintegrates, or burns, making carbon dioxide and water; but if the heating is done where the oxygen is excluded, as in a kiln, the hydrogen and oxygen will be driven off and the carbon will remain behind as charcoal. In Nature similar reactions go on, but more slowly. Vegetable matter, exposed to the air, disintegrates into carbon dioxide and water, and there is no solid residue. However, if the vegetable matter is under water, which excludes the air more or less completely including the oxygen in it, then disintegration still takes place, but the products formed are water, (H_2O) marsh gas (CH_4), and some carbon dioxide (CO_2), but a considerable part of the carbon remains behind and accumulates.

Thus in bogs, swamps and ponds, where dead vegetation, especially that growing in the water, piles up, the oxidation is incomplete; so that there gradually accumulates on the bottom a layer of brown to black mud, known as *peat*. More plant remains are constantly being added, and the layer may increase to several feet in thickness. The decomposition is incomplete and some oxygen and hydrogen remain, but the carbon is in a constantly increasing ratio and in proportion far above that in cellulose. In the cold northern climates sphagnum moss is the most efficient peat producing plant, but in temperate and tropical climates the moss is replaced by the leaves, twigs, trunks, etc., of trees, bushes, and vines.

If these peat beds are buried beneath a layer or layers of sediment, especially clay, the peat is sealed up and oxidation stops almost entirely. With the pressure of the superincumbent beds, the peat becomes more and more compact, and changes to a dark-brown or black color. It is then known as *lignite*. If this lignite is buried still deeper, with consequently more pressure and more time, it changes into the still denser black *bituminous coal*. This is as far as it will go unless some new agent is added to the forces already working.

The next step in the series of changes forming coal is associated with mountain making. In case the layers of rock containing beds of coal are folded, and that presupposes at least a moderate increase in heat, the bituminous coal is altered to *anthracite*, which is still denser, and so hard that it breaks with a conchoidal fracture. Alteration may be carried a step still farther, in case the rocks between which lie beds of coal are effected by such high temperatures as accompany metamorphism. Then all the associated hydrogen, oxygen and moisture are driven off, and only the carbon remains, which is then known as *graphite*. All steps between the stages especially designated occur. The following represent steps only in the series of changes.

Peat   Peat is a mass of unconsolidated vegetable matter, which has accumulated under water, and in which the original plant remains are still, at least in part, discernible. It contains a large amount of water, so that before it can be used as a fuel, it is cut out in blocks, which are piled up and left for a time to dry before using. It burns with a long flame and considerable smoke. This country is so well supplied with other fuels, that so far peat has been but little used

Lignite
brown coal   Lignite is more compact than peat, and is found buried to some depth under layers of clay or sandstone. It is dark brown to black in color, and still retains pretty clear traces of the plants from which it was derived. It also usually contains a considerable amount of moisture, and when this is dried out, it tends to crumble badly, so that it is undesirable to handle it much, or to ship it far, before using. It has a fair fuel value and is fairly widely used; but it is very desirable that some method be found, by which lignite could be treated to obtain its by-products, and at the same time make it more compact, so it would

not crumble with the handling incident to using it in furnaces. There are extensive lignite deposits in this country in North and South Dakota, Montana, Wyoming, Colorado, New Mexico, Texas, Louisiana, and Mississippi.

Bituminous Coal *soft coal* This type of coal is compact, black in color, and breaks readily, but does not crumble as badly as lignite. It contains considerable water, and still has some hydrogen and oxygen compounds in it. Bituminous coal is the product of plant remains which have been preserved for long periods, (millions of years), sealed from the air by the overlying beds of rock. The pressure has made it compact, and nearly all traces of the original plants have disappeared.

Bituminous coal is our most abundant fuel, occurring the world over in seams from less than an inch in thickness to some over fifteen feet thick. The United States is peculiarly fortunate in the abundant and easily accessible deposits of this type of coal, in Pennsylvania, West Virginia, Ohio, Kentucky, Tennessee, Indiana, Illinois, Michigan, Iowa, Missouri, Kansas, Nebraska, Texas, Utah, and Colorado.

The volatile constituents, hydrogen and oxygen compounds, of bituminous coal may be driven off by heating the coal in closed ovens, and the residual mass is known as *coke*, almost pure carbon. This is distillation, and the ovens in which this is done, without trying to save the volatile products, are called bee-hive ovens, while the more modern ovens which save the by-products are called by-products ovens. A ton of bituminous coal treated in the typical by-products oven, will yield on the average 1410 lb. of coke, 7.1 gallons of tar, 18.9 pounds of ammonia sulphate, etc., 2.4 gallons of light oils, 10440 cubic feet of illuminating gas, about half of this last being used to furnish the heat for the distillation. The coal-tar dye industry is built on the tar thus produced. Toluol, benzol, etc., come from the light oils; and half the gas produced is available for household illumination, etc. Coke is demanded, as it is a superior fuel for melting iron ores, iron and steel, and is made regardless of whether the by-products are used. The coke thus produced is hard, clean, and vesicular; but for some reason as yet unknown, by no means all bituminous coal will produce a coke which has this porous structure. These latter are known as "non-coking," and are of little use to the steel industry.

Cannel Coal This is a compact variety of non-coking bituminous coal, with a dull luster and a conchoidal fracture. It contains the largest proportion of volatile hydrocarbon compounds of any variety of coal; so that when the supply of petroleum and natural gas gives out, this will be one of the important sources of obtaining substitutes. Cannel coals occur in Ohio, Indiana, and eastern Kentucky. This cannel coal owes its peculiar fatty nature to the material from which it is derived, it being supposed to have resulted from the accumulation of the spores of lycopod trees, and their conversion to jelly-like masses by bacteria in the fresh-water marshes of those ancient days

Anthracite
hard coal
Anthracite coal is hard, black, has a high luster, and breaks with a conchoidal fracture. It contains but a low percentage of volatile matter, and so burns with a short flame, and less smoke, than is the case with the other coals. It is always associated with folded rocks, and appears to have been formed as a result of the combined pressure and the higher temperatures, which accompanied mountain making. Still the temperature was not high enough to metamorphose the adjacent rocks. Most of our anthracite comes from northeastern Pennsylvania.

Carbonite
Carbonite is natural coke. It occurs in coal seams which have been cut by dikes or intrusions of igneous rocks, the coal having been thus coked by natural processes. It is not vesicular like artificial coke, for which reason it is not useful as a fuel. Some carbonite is found in the Cerillos coal field of New Mexico, in Colorado, and Virginia.

Jet
Jet is a dense variety of lignite, a fossil wood of black color, which takes a high polish and cuts easily into various ornamental shapes. It has been used for ornaments since early ancient times, beads of jet being found in the early bronze period in England, the supply probably coming from the Yorkshire coast, whence the principal supply

comes even to the present day. In Switzerland and Belgium it was used still earlier, even as far back as the Palæolithic age. Jet seems then to have had a talismanic value, and to have been worn to protect the owner. About 700 A.D. crosses and rosaries began to be made of jet, the custom starting at Whitby Abbey, the material being obtained nearby, so that it came to be known as "Whitby jet," and in the eighteenth century became very popular. In recent times it has been used mostly as jewelry suitable for mourning.

Amber
Pl. 61

Amber is a gum which oozed from coniferous trees and was petrified. It is associated with lignite beds of middle Tertiary age. It is usually pale-yellow in color, but at times has a reddish or brownish tinge, and is more or less transparent. It occurs in rounded irregular lumps, up to ten pounds in weight, though most pieces are smaller; and is mostly picked up along certain coasts where it is washed ashore by the waves. Since the earliest records amber has been cast up on the shores of the Baltic, and it was used by peoples as early as in the stone age for ornaments and amulets. It has been found among the remains of the cave dwellers of Switzerland, in Assyrian and Egyptian ruins of prehistoric age, and in Mycenæ in the prehistoric graves of the Greeks, the first recorded reference to it being in Homer, and the Greek name for amber being *elektron* from which our word electricity comes. All these finds were of Baltic amber which was doubtless gathered and traded by those early men. Even down to the present many men make their living, riding along the shore at low tide and hunting for the amber washed ashore by the waves. As early as 1860 the German geologists concluded that the source of the amber must be lignite beds outcropping beneath the sea level, and started mining for the amber with fair success, so that today two types of Baltic amber are distinguished, "sea stone" which is washed ashore, and "mine stone" taken from the mines. Beside the Baltic locality, it is found along the shores of the Adriatic, Sicily, France, China, and occasionally of North America.

Some pieces of amber are found with insects inclosed and preserved almost as perfectly as if collected yesterday. They were apparently entangled in the gum while still viscid and completely embedded, before fossilization.

THE PETROLEUM SERIES

Certain sedimentary rocks contain larger or smaller quantities of natural gas, petroleum, mineral tar and asphalt. These are compounds of carbon and hydrogen, or hydrocarbons, and range from gases to solids, each being a mixture of two or more hydrocarbon compounds. The crude petroleum may have either a paraffin base or an asphalt base: in the former case, when the gas, gasoline, kerosene, etc., have been removed by distillation, the solid residue will be paraffin, as in most of the Pennsylvania crude oils; while in the latter case, the solid residue will be an asphalt, as in most of the California and Texas crude oils. In the case of the paraffin series all the compounds belong to the paraffin group, while the asphalt is due to the presence, in addition to the paraffin group, of some of the benzine series of hydrocarbons.

Petroleum is found in sands and shales, which were originally deposited on ancient sea bottoms, the shales generally being the real source of the petroleum. The oil was once the fatty portion of animal bodies (perhaps to some extent of plant bodies), and was separated during decomposition as a result of bacterial activity. Oil thus produced is in tiny droplets, which have a great affinity for clay. After being freed by the bacteria, the oil droplets in muddy water attach themselves to particles of clay, and as the clay settles the oil is carried down with it, the two eventually making a bituminous shale. In clear water, or in water which is in motion, the oil droplets rise to the surface and eventually distill into the air.

The oil, or petroleum, may stay diffused through the shales, in which case we have *oil-bearing shales*, with sometimes as much as 20% of oil. Were there but $\frac{1}{1000}$ of a per cent of oil in a layer of shale 1500 feet thick, this would amount to 750,000 barrels per square mile which is equal to a rich production from wells. When the oil in shale amounts to three per cent or more, it is commercially usable. There are large stretches of petroleum-bearing rocks in New York, Pennsylvania, Ohio, Indiana, and all the way out to the Pacific coast, some of them with oil so abundant, that a blow of the hammer will cause them to smell of petroleum.

In case these oil-bearing shales have been heavily overburdened and compressed, the petroleum may have been more or less completely pressed out of them. Then the droplets uniting have formed a liquid, which has moved out from the shale, and gone wherever it could find open spaces. Sandstones have frequently offered their pore space, and as it filled, have been thus saturated with petroleum. If the sandstones were open to the air, or if fissures extended from them to the surface, the oil has escaped to the surface and evaporated into the air. But in those cases where the sandstone (or other permeable rocks) was covered by an impervious layer, like a dense shale or clay, the oil was confined below the covering layer of rock. Crude oil is lighter than water; so that when natural gas, petroleum and water were all present in the rocks, the gas lies on top, the petroleum next, and the water underneath. With this in mind it is easy to see, that in slightly folded or undulating layers of rock, the gas and petroleum would be caught under upraised folds and domes. This is the basis of prospecting for oil.

If petroleum-bearing layers are depressed far enough beneath the surface to be affected by the high temperatures of the earth's interior, or have been near volcanic activity, of course the petroleum has been distilled by natural processes, and at most only the residues, like paraffin or asphalt, have remained. For this reason it is impossible to find petroleum in igneous or meta-morphic rocks.

Natural gas   Natural gas is the lightest portion of crude oil, and consists mostly of marsh gas ("fire damp," CH_4) together with other light hydrocarbons, like ethane (C_2H_6), ethylene (C_2H_4), and some carbon dioxide and monoxide. It is colorless, odorless, and burns with a luminous flame. Mixed with air it is explosive. It is found in sedimentary rocks, mostly sandstones, either with or without petroleum. Usually it is under considerable pressure, and escapes with great force wherever a hole permits. In time the gas all escapes through the hole or well, and then the well "runs out." If petroleum is present under the natural gas, the hole may become an "oil well," from which petroleum may be pumped, until it in turn is exhausted. The end of an oil supply is usually indicated by the appearance of water in the well. Natural gas is mostly associated with oil districts, as in Pennsylvania, Ohio, Illinois, Texas, California, etc.

Petroleum   Petroleum is a mixture of paraffin
Crude Oil   compounds all the way from the
Pl. 61   gases, through gasoline, kerosene, lubricating oils, and vasoline to paraffin. In some of the crude oils there is also an admixture of compounds from the benzine series, in which case, when all the volatile compounds have been distilled off, an asphalt remains. The different components of petroleum may be separated out

by heating the crude oil in closed tanks, and drawing off the various substances at the proper temperatures.

Petroleum occurs in sedimentary rocks of marine origin, usually rocks which also contain the shells of some of the animals, the soft parts of which made the oil. To have been preserved the millions of years since the petroleum was first formed, the oil-bearing layers must have been covered by some impervious layer of rock, beneath the domes and anticlines of which the oil has lain ever since. When such a dome or anticlinal fold is perforated by a well, the released oil flows to the surface with a greater or less rush, according to the pressure. Wells may keep flowing for 20 years, sometimes more, sometimes much less. Those which flow with the greatest pressure usually are relatively short lived, at times lasting only a year or two. When this easily obtained oil is exhausted, there is an even greater supply to be obtained by the distillation of the bituminous shales. Petroleum never occurs in igneous or metamorphic rocks, but is found in either sandstones or shales, in places favorable for accumulation, all across that great stretch of ancient sea bottoms, extending from the Appalachian Mountains to the Rocky Mountains, and in the Great Basin between the Rocky Mountains and the Sierra Nevada Range, and also to the west of the Sierras.

Bitumen   Where petroleum has escaped through pores in the rocks, or by way of fissures, and has come to the surface of the earth, the lighter components, thus exposed to the air, have vaporized and escaped, leaving behind a more or less solid residue, which is known as bitumen. If the escape was through a fissure, the bitumen may have accumulated in the fissure until it was filled, making vein bitumen. Or the escape may have been so rapid that the petroleum formed a pool or lake from the surface of which evaporation took place. In time such a pool will give off the gases and volatile compounds, only a residue remaining to make a pitch lake, like the one at Rancho Le Brea near Los Angeles, or an asphalt lake like the one on the island of Trinidad. On account of their varying hardness and composition, some of these bitumens have received special names; as:

Albertite, a black bitumen with a brilliant luster on broken surfaces, a hardness between 1 and 2, and a specific gravity a shade over 1.

Grahamite, a black bitumen, which is brittle, but has a dull luster, a hardness of 2, and a specific gravity of 1.15.

Gilsonite or **Uintaite,** a black bitumen with a brilliant luster and a conchoidal fracture, a hardness of 2 to 2½, and a specific gravity of 1.06.

Malta is a semi-liquid viscid natural bitumen, which has a considerable distribution in California.

The above varieties of bitumen look a good deal like coal, but are easily distinguished by their lightness (weight about half that of coal), and the fact that with only moderate heat they melt, and become a thick liquid like tar.

Guano   Guano is the accumulation of the excrement of birds (or of other animals like bats) on areas so dry that, though soluble, it is not leached and washed away. It may also contain some of the bones and mummified carcasses of the birds which died on the spot. The greatest of these deposits are on several small islands, just off the west coast of Peru, and now "farmed" by the Peruvian government. In this country there are no true guano beds, except a few accumulations of bat guano in certain caves of Kentucky and Texas, but these are not large enough to become of commercial importance.

Phosphate Rock   Phosphate rock is one composed chiefly of calcium phosphate along with various impurities, such as clay and lime. It occurs in beds, irregular masses, or as concretionary nodules in limestone or sand.

The bedded varieties are in the older sedimentary rocks, in which the phosphate runs from a small percentage up to as high as 85%. Ultimately the phosphate came from either animal excrement, or from bacterial decomposition of animal carcasses and bones. In all the beds it seems to be true that in the first instance the phosphate was laid down as a disseminated deposit in marine beds, usually limestones. Later by the action of water leaching through the rocks, the phosphate was dissolved, and then redeposited elsewhere in a more concentrated form. This may be either in the underlying sandstones, but is more often in limestones, replacing the original lime.

In these secondary deposits, if the phosphate has been laid down in cavities, the resulting phosphate will be in nodular masses. In the case of the Florida and Carolina deposits, these nodules have been freed from their matrix and washed along the river beds, remaining as pebbles in the river sands. The bed deposits are mostly in Kentucky and Idaho. The commercial use for such phosphate rocks is of course the making of fertilizers.

Diatomaceous Earth
Pl. 62
Diatoms are tiny single-celled plants living in uncounted millions in the fresh and salt water. Each diatom builds around itself two shells which fit into each other like the cover and box of a pill-box, and each shell is marvelously ornamented. The shells are composed of silica of the opal type. In size the diatoms range from $\frac{1}{5000}$ of an inch in diameter up to the size of a pin head, and they live in such numbers that ordinary surface waters have hundreds of them to the quart, and where they are flourishing up to 250,000 in a quart. When the plants die, or in order to reproduce abandon the shells, these shells fall to the bottom of the pond or the sea, and there accumulate, often making a layer from a few inches thick up to hundreds of feet in extreme cases. If unconsolidated, this mass of tiny shells is known as diatomaceous earth; but if they are consolidated it is called tripolite, so named because the first of them used commercially came from Tripoli.

As the shells are tiny and uniform in size and

have a hardness of 6, the diatomaceous earth is used to make a great variety of polishes, scouring soaps, tooth paste, as a filler in certain kinds of paper, in making waterglass, as an absorbent for nitroglycerine, and as packing in insulating compounds, where asbestos would otherwise be used.

Deposits of freshwater diatoms are found all over the United States, usually in thin layers of limited extent, especially in Massachusetts, New York, Michigan, etc. The marine deposits of diatoms are on a much larger scale, there being beds of diatoms in Anne Arundel, Calvert and Charles Counties, Md., up to 25 or 30 feet in thickness. In Santa Barbara County, Cal., there is one bed 2400 feet thick and another 4700 feet thick, beside many other smaller ones. The enormous former wealth of life indicated by these great deposits may be suggested, when it is remembered that it takes about 120,000,000 to make an ounce in weight. They reproduce on an average about once in five days, so that from a single diatom the offspring possible under favorable conditions would amount to over 16,000,000 in four months or over 60 tons in a year. Of such an order is the potential increase of animals or plants, no matter how small, if the rate of reproduction is high.

METAMORPHIC ROCKS

Either a sedimentary or an igneous rock, which has been altered by the combined activities of heat, pressure and chemical action, becomes a metamorphic rock. The process is essentially one, during which the layers of rock come under the influence of such temperatures as are associated with the formation of granite or lavas. Such material as is actually melted becomes igneous rock, but adjacent to the masses actually melted are other rocks which do not melt but, according to the temperature, are more or less changed, and these are the metamorphic rocks. At a distance from the molten masses the changes are minor, but close to the molten magmas extensive changes take place. Though not actually melted the rock near the heat center may be softened, usually is, in which case pebbles and grains or even crystals become soft and plastic, and, as a result of the great pressure, are flattened, giving the rock, when it cools again, a striated appearance. At these high temperatures the water in the rock and also some other substances vaporize, and the hot steam and vapor are active agents in making a great many chemical changes. In some cases material like clay is changed into micas, or chlorite, etc.; in other cases the elements of a mineral will be segregated and large crystals will appear scattered through the metamorphic rock, such as garnets, staurolites, etc.

If one studies a layer of rock both near and far from the molten mass, all grades of change will appear. For example, at a distance a conglomerate maybe unaltered; somewhat nearer the molten mass, the heat and steam may have softened (but not melted) the pebbles and then the pressure has flattened them as though they were dough; and nearest the molten mass, the outlines of the pebbles are lost, only a layered effect remaining, and many of the materials have changed into new minerals, like mica, garnets, etc., but still the layered effect is preserved.

One of the effects of heat and pressure is to flatten the component particles of the rock, so that it tends to split in a direction at right angles to the direction of the pressure, just as particles of flour are softened and flattened under the pressure of the roller; and then when the crust is baked it splits or cleaves at right angles to the direction in which the pressure was exerted by the roller. This tendency to split is not to be confused with either the layering, characteristic of sedimentary rocks, nor the cleavage characteristic of minerals. It has nothing to do with the way the particles were originally deposited, nor with their cleavage; but is due to the pressure, and resembles the pie crust splitting, being irregular and flaky. This is designated *schistosity* if irregular and *slaty cleavage* if regular. Schistosity refers to the flaky manner of splitting into thin scales as in mica schists. Slaty cleavage is more regular, this being due to the fact that the material of which slate is made is small particles of clay of uniform size.

The metamorphic rocks are generally more or less folded, as they are always associated with mountain making. These major folds are of large size, from a hundred feet across to several miles from one side to the other. Such folds may also occur in sedimentary rocks or even in igneous rocks and simply express the great lines of yielding, or movement of the crust of the earth. In

addition to this there is minor folding or contort-
ing which is characteristic of metamorphic rocks
only. When the rocks were heated by their
nearness to the molten igneous magmas, they
must expand, but being overburdened by thick
layers of other rocks, there is no opportunity for
yielding vertically, so the layers crumple, making
minor folds from a fraction of an inch to a few
feet across. Such crumpling, which is so very
conspicuous especially where there are bands of
quartzite in the rock, is entirely characteristic of
metamorphic rocks. It is seen on hosts of the
rocks about New York City, all over New England, and in any other metamorphic region.
Plate 63 is a photograph of such a crumpled rock
which has been smoothed by the glacial ice.

The metamorphic rocks are the most difficult
of all the rocks to determine and understand,
because the amount of change through which
they have gone is greatest, but for this same
reason they offer the most interest, for the
agents which caused the changes are of the most
dramatic type of any that occur in Nature.
From one place to another a single layer of metamorphic rock changes according to the greater
or less heat to which it was subjected, making
a series of related rocks of the same composition
but with varied amount of alteration. For this
reason in naming metamorphic rocks, a type is
named, and from that there will be gradations
in one or more directions, both according to
composition, and according to amount of heat
involved. If it is possible to follow a given layer
of metamorphic rock from one place to another

this is of great interest; for by this means, many variations in the type will be found, both those resulting from a different amount of heat, and those due to the local changes in the composition of the original rock.

One further consideration has to be kept in mind. When a rock is metamorphosed the high temperatures either drive off all water, or the water may be used up in the making of some of the complex minerals. When such a meta-morphic rock later comes near the surface and is exposed to the presence of ground water, and that leaching down from the surface into the rocks, several of the minerals formed at high temperatures will take up this water and make new minerals such as serpentine, chlorite, etc. They are always associated with metamorphic rocks, and have been metamorphic rocks, but since then have become hydrated, forming miner-als not at all characteristic of high temperature.

The following shows the relation of the sedimentary and igneous rocks to their meta-morphic equivalents.

Loose sediment	Consolidated sediment	Metamorphic equivalent
gravel	conglomerate	gneiss
sand (quartz)	sandstone	quartzite
mud (sand and clay)	shale	schist
clay	shale	slate or phyllite
marl	limestone	marble
peat	bituminous coal	anthracite to graphite
	coarse igneous rocks such as granite, syenite, etc.	gneiss
	fine igneous rocks such as trachite, rhyolite, etc.	schist

In working out the past history of any given region, much of it is done on the basis of this series of equivalents. The finding of limestone, for instance, indicates that the given area was at one time under the sea to a considerable depth, that is from 100 to 1000 feet, but not ocean-bottom depths which run in tens of thousands of feet. Marble indicates the same thing, and so one can go on through all these types of rock.

Gneiss
Pl. 64
Gneiss is an old word used by the Saxon miners, and is often very loosely used. Here it is used in its structural sense, and a gneiss may be defined as: a banded metamorphic rock, derived either from a sedimentary or an igneous rock, and is composed of feldspar, quartz, and mica or hornblende, and is coarse enough, so that the constituent minerals can be determined by the eye. It corresponds to a granite, or some sedimentary rock like gravel or conglomerate.

Due to the action of pressure, all the gneisses are banded, and the original constituent particles or crystals are distorted. The lines of banding may be long or short, straight, curved or contorted. When the banding is not conspicuous, the gneiss tends toward a granite. When the banding is thin and the structure appears flaky, the gneiss tends toward a schist. The color varies according to the constituent minerals, from nearly white, through red, gray, brown, or green to nearly black. Plate 64 shows one gneiss which is in a less advanced stage, the pebbles being simply flattened and the matrix partly altered to micaceous minerals, and a second gneiss which is so far advanced that the original constituents are all altered to other minerals and only the banded structure remains. This latter type would have required but little more heat to have completed the melting and changed this to a granite.

Gneisses are very compact and have little or no pore space in them. They are hard and strong and resist weathering well, so that they are widely used as building stone; but they are not as good as granite for this purpose, as they split more readily in one direction and can not therefore be worked so uniformly as can granite.

There are many varieties of gneiss, based either on their origin, composition, or their structure, as follows.

Granite-gneiss is one derived by metamorphism from granite.

Syenite-gneiss is one derived by metamorphism from syenite.

Diorite-gneiss is one derived by metamorphism from diorite.

Gabbro-gneiss is one derived by metamorphism from gabbro.

Biotite-gneiss is one composed of quartz, feldspar and biotite.

Muscovite-gneiss is one composed of quartz, feldspar and muscovite.

Hornblende-gneiss is one composed of quartz, feldspar and hornblende.

Banded-gneiss is one in which the banded structure shows clearly.

Foliated-gneiss is one in which there is thin irregular layering.

Augen-gneiss is one which has concretionary lumps scattered through it.

Gneisses have a wide distribution over all New England, most of Canada, the Piedmont Plateau, the Lake Superior region, the Rocky Mountains, the Sierra Nevada and the Cascade Ranges

Quartzite   Quartzite is metamorphosed sand or sandstone, and frequently grades into one or the other. It is a hard compact crystalline rock, which breaks with a splintery or choncoidal fracture. It is distinguished from sandstone by the almost complete lack of pore spaces, its greater hardness and by its crystalline structure. In practice it may be distinguished by the fact that a sandstone in breaking separates between the grains of sand, while a quartzite breaks through the grains.

Some quartzites are almost pure quartz, but others contain impurities of clay, lime or iron, which were in the original sandstone. These alter in the metamorphism to such accessory minerals as feldspar, mica, cyanite, magnetite, hematite, calcite, graphite, etc. The color of quartzite when pure is white, but may be altered to red, yellow, or green by the presence of these accessory minerals.

On account of the difficulty of working the quartzites, they are not much used in building, though they are very durable. When crushed they often make excellent road ballast, or filling for concrete work. The pure varieties are sometimes ground and used in the manufacture of glass.

According to the accessory mineral, the following varieties may be distinguished; chloritic-quartzite, micaceous-quartzite, feldspathic-quartzite, etc.

Quartzites are common in the New England, the Piedmont Plateau, and Lake Superior metamorphic regions, and also in many western localities.

Schist
Pl. 65

Schist is a loosely used term, but is used here in its structural sense. It includes those metamorphic rocks which are foliated or composed of thin scaly layers, all more or less alike. The principle minerals are recognizable with the naked eye. In general schists lack feldspar, but there are some special cases in which it may be present. Quartz is an abundant component of schists; and with it there will be one or more minerals of the following groups, mica, chlorite, talc, amphibole, or pyroxene. Frequently there are also accessory minerals present, like garnet, staurolite, tourmaline, pyrite, magnetite, etc.

All schists have the schistose structure, and split in one direction with a more or less smooth, though often irregular, surface. At right angles to this surface they break with greater or less difficulty and with a frayed edge. As they get coarser, the schists may grade into gneisses, losing their scaly structure: while on the other side, as the constituent minerals become finer and so small as to be difficult of recognition, schists may grade into slates.

The varieties of schist are based on the mineral associated with the quartz; as mica-schist, chlorite-schist, hornblende-schist, talc-schist, etc.

The color also is due to the constituent minerals other than quartz and ranges widely, mica-schists being white to brown or nearly black, chlorite-schists some shade of green, hornblende-schists from dark green to black, talc-schists white, pale-green, yellowish or gray, etc.

Schists are found all over the same regions as gneisses and quartzites, *i.e.*, New England (especially good exposures of schist being seen about New York City), the Lake Superior region, Rocky Mountains, etc. Beside these regions where it occurs native, there are boulders of schist all over the glaciated areas of eastern and northern United States.

Slate   Slate is a metamorphic rock which will split into thin or thick sheets, and is composed of grains so fine as to be indistinguishable to the unaided eye. The cleavage is the result of pressure during metamorphism, and has nothing to do with the bedding or stratification of the sedimentary rock from which it was derived. The original bedding planes may appear as streaks, often more or less plicated, and running at any angle with the cleavage. If these bedding streaks are abundant or very marked, they may make a slate unsuitable for commercial uses. The slaty cleavage may be very perfect and smooth so that the rock splits into fine sheets, in which case it is often used for roofing slate; but by far the greater part of the slates have a cleavage which is not smooth or perfect enough so that they can be so used. Slates are the metamorphic equivalents of shales and muds, and represent the effect of great pressure but with less heat than is associated with schists or phyllite, and consequently with less alteration of the original mineral grains.

The color ranges from gray through red, green and purple to black. The grays and black are due to the presence of more or less carbonaceous material in the original rock, the carbon compounds having changed to graphite. The reds and purple are due to the presence of iron oxides, and the green to the presence of chlorite.

While the particles of slate are so small as to be indistinguishable to the unaided eye, the use of thin sections under the microscope shows that slate is composed mostly of quartz and mica, with a wide range of accessory minerals, like chlorite, feldspar, magnetite, hematite, pyrite, calcite, graphite, etc.

According to their chief constituents slates may be distinguished as argillaceous-slate or *argillite*, bituminous-slate, calcareous-slate, siliceous-slate, etc.

Slate will be found here and there in the metamorphic areas of New England, the Piedmont Plateau, the Lake Superior region, and in many places in the west.

Phyllite
Pl. 66

Phyllite is a thinly cleavable, finely micaceous rock of uniform composition, which is intermediate between slate and mica schist. In this case the flakes of mica are large enough to be distinguishable to the eye, but most of the rest of the material can only be identified with the aid of a microscope. It is mostly quartz and sericite. Phyllite represents a degree of metamorphism greater than for slate, but less than for schist; and it may grade into either of these other rocks. Garnets, pyrite, etc., may be present as accessory minerals. The color ranges from nearly white to black, and it is likely to occur in the same places as do slates.

Marble
Pl. 66

This is a broad term, and includes all those rocks composed essentially of calcium carbonate (limestones) or its mixture with magnesium carbonate (dolomite), which are crystalline, or of granular structure, as a result of metamorphism. It takes less heat to metamorphose a limestone, and for this reason the marbles have a more crystalline structure than most metamorphic rocks; and they do not have the tendency to split or cleave which is so characteristic of most metamorphic rocks. It is only when there is a large amount of mica present that the typical schistosity appears. Commercially the term marble is used to include true marble and also those limestones which will take a high polish; but in this book, and geologically speaking, no rock is a marble unless it has crystalline structure.

Marbles range widely in color according to their impurities. Pure marble is white. Carbonaceous material in the antecedent limestone is changed to graphite in the metamorphic process, and makes the marble black, but appears usually in streaks or spots, rather than in any uniform color. An all black "marble" is usually a limestone. The presence of iron colors the marble red or pink. Chlorite makes it green, etc.

Various accessory minerals are common in marbles, such as mica, pyroxene, amphibole, grossularite among the garnets, magnetite, spinel, pyrite, etc., through a long list.

Because it cuts readily in all directions and takes a high polish, marble is widely used as a building stone. In the moist climate of the United States it suffers in being soluble in rain water when used on the outside of a building: but for interior decoration it furnishes some of the finest effects.

The largest marble quarries are developed in Vermont, Massachusetts, New York, Pennsylvania, Georgia, Alabama, Colorado, California, and Washington.

Steatite
Soapstone

Steatite is a rock composed essentially of talc, which is associated with more or less impurities, such as mica, tremolite, enstatite, quartz, magnetite, etc. It is found in and with metamorphic rocks, and is a rock which has been modified by hydration from a metamorphic predecessor. It was probably first a tremolite or enstatite schist, in which, after the metamorphic rock came into the zone where ground water exists, the tremolite or enstatite was altered to talc, the impurities remaining much as they were in the first place.

It is bluish-gray to green in color, often soft enough to cut with a knife, and has a greasy feel. It is very resistant to heat and acids; for which reasons it has proved very useful commercially in making hearthstones, laundry tubs, and fire backs; and, when powdered, in making certain lubricants. The Indians, in the days before Columbus, took advantage of the ease with which it is cut, to make from it large pots for holding liquids, which are today among the greatest treasures in collections of Indian relics. They also carved pipe-bowls and various ornaments and amulets from soapstone.

It is found in Vermont, Massachusetts, New York, New Jersey, Pennsylvania, Maryland, Virginia, North Carolina, Georgia and California.

Serpentine
Pl. 67

Pure serpentine is the hydrated silicate of magnesium, as described among the minerals on page 138. Serpentine rock is serpentine with more or less impurities, such as pyroxene, amphibole, olivine, magnetite, chromite, calcite, magnesite, etc. It often also contains mica and such garnets as pyrope, as accessory minerals. Serpentine, like steatite, always occurs in and with metamorphic rocks, and was originally a metamorphic rock, but has since been changed by the hydration of its silicates, when it came into the zone in which ground water is present. In the first instance it was some sort of shale, clay and dolomite, which was metamorphosed to an amphibole or pyroxene schist. When this was exposed to the action of ground water, the amphibole or pyroxene minerals were changed to serpentine, resulting in a rock composed mostly of serpentine, but retaining the impurities which were in the metamorphic rock, and perhaps adding to them such amphiboles and pyroxenes as were not altered during the hydration process. The above is the commonest type of serpentine rock. It can and sometimes has been formed in a similar way from an igneous predecessor, by the hydration of its silicate minerals. In this latter case the serpentine would not be a modified metamorphic rock, but a modified igneous one. It is a case where such a rock as a diorite or a gabbro is exposed to ground water and the pyroxene present altered to serpentine. A serpentine formed in this way would be a very impure one.

Serpentine rock is used as an ornamental stone for interior decoration, because it takes a high polish and has pleasing colors, various shades of green. It is however decidedly soft and will stand very little exposure to weather, and it is also filled with seams which make it difficult to get out large slabs.

Serpentine rock occurs fairly commonly in the metamorphic belt of New England and the Piedmont Plateau, and in some of the western states, especially California, Oregon, and Washington.

Ophiolite
Ophicalcite This name is given to marbles which are streaked and spotted with serpentine. They are a mixture of green serpentine and a white or nearly white

calcite, magnesite or dolomite in variable proportions.

Ophicalcite occurs in and with metamorphic rocks, and represents an impure limestone which has been metamorphised, the lime becoming marble, and the impurities becoming such silicates as pyroxene, amphibole, or olivine. This metamorphic rock has then come into the zone of ground-water and the silicate minerals have been changed by hydration to serpentine. Ophicalcite is then a metamorphic rock, in which secondary chemical changes have since taken place. It may have a wide range of accessory minerals present, such as magnetite, chromite, pyrope among the garnets, olivine, etc. Verde antique is a trade name for one of the ophiolites.

While not abundant, ophicalcite is in good demand as an ornamental stone for interior work; for it takes a high polish, and is beautiful; but, on the other hand, it will not stand exposure to the weather for the calcite is soluble, and there are numerous seams and cracks in it making it difficult to obtain large slabs.

It occurs in Quebec, Canada, in the Green Mountains of Vermont, and in the Adirondack Mountains.

CHAPTER V

MISCELLANEOUS ROCKS

There are a few rocks which do not fit into any of the three groups described, such as concretions, geodes, meteorites, etc., and they are gathered together here. There is also one type of rock, which really belongs among the minerals, but is likely not to be so recognized at first glance, and that is the material filling veins. These last are sometimes designated "vein rocks," but are really massive deposits of one, two or more minerals, and should be referred to the minerals when found.

CONCRETIONS

In the sedimentary rocks there frequently occur inclusions of a nature different from the surrounding rock. In shape they are usually rounded, nodular, spherical, discoidal, ovate, flattened, elongated or ring-shaped, or combinations of the foregoing, making often curious and fantastic forms. In size they range from a fraction of an inch in diameter to several feet through. When broken, they may show a nucleus, around which more or less concentric layers have formed, or neither nucleus nor concentric structure may be visible. The layered structure of the surrounding rock in some cases continues right through the nodular mass. These structures are called concretions, and their formation in all cases is at least due to similar reactions.

In general the concretions differ from the surrounding rock in composition, but are usually composed of some one of its impurities, of lime in the clays or silica in limestones, of iron oxide in sandstone, etc. They seem to have originated as a result of the solution of the minor mineral, and then its redeposition around some center or nucleus. In many cases the nucleus is organic, such as a leaf, a shell, a bone, etc., so that when the concretion is split, in its center will be found the perfect imprint of the leaf, or the shell of a mollusk, or a bone of a higher animal, sometimes a whole skeleton. Again the nucleus may be inorganic like a grain of sand; and in still other cases no nucleus can be found, though there was probably one in the beginning. What has happened is somewhat like the case of accessory minerals in igneous and metamorphic rocks. A layer of sediment was laid down, including in it, here and there, something foreign to the run of the rock. Later when the water leaches through this rock, impregnated with lime for instance, it comes to the point where a leaf is decomposing. The products of the leaf decomposition are different from what is already present in solution, and may precipitate some of the lime in that neighborhood. As long as leaf decomposition continues the precipitation in that region will continue and increase the size of the concretion. This sort of action accounts for many of the concretions, especially those about organic remains. In some other cases where there is no nucleus, as the flint in chalk, what has taken place is that the small amounts of silica in the lime have been dissolved, and then around some center has constantly been added more and more non-crystalline silica until a mass of flint has accumulated. There may be a considerable variety of ways to account for different concretions, but in all cases solutions of one mineral have come in contact with solutions of a different kind, and precipitation about a center has resulted.

Clay stones
Pl. 68
Of all the concretions these are perhaps the commonest, being found in the clays of all types and in many regions. They are made of lime and precipitated around some nucleus of foreign matter. The shapes vary widely, usually discs, flattened ovals or even rings, in most all cases however flattened. This is indicative of the water moving though the clay more freely in some layers than others. Often clay stones occur so abundantly that two or more have grown together making fantastic shapes, sometimes resembling animals, and all sorts of fancied but unrelated objects. As the clay stones have grown the clay has not been pushed aside, but has been incorporated within the concretion; so that when a concretion is dissolved in acid, it yields not only the lime,

which is its reason for being, but also a large amount of clay.

Claystones are found in clays most anywhere, usually occurring in certain layers and being absent from others.

Lime concretions These are found mostly in shales which carry a high percentage of clay as impurities, and are characteristic of the older geological formations, especially ancient sea bottoms. They are likely to have as a nucleus some shell, fish bone, or a leaf, which when the concretion is split, reveals a wonderfully preserved portion of an animal or a plant, which was buried millions of years ago. The lime concretion is closely related to the claystone, and is really a claystone which has been buried so long that the surrounding matrix has changed to a shale instead of remaining clay.

One of the most famous localities for these lime concretions is Mazon Creek, Illinois, where thousands of these concretions have been picked up and split to study the organic remains included. The commonest objects found are fern leaves, like the one on Plate 68. But about once in a thousand times they inclose a spider or insect, and once in ten thousand times the skeleton of an amphibian, which is of especial interest, as here have been thus found the remains of the very earliest of the land animals. These remains were inclosed in these concretions during the coal age, probably 50,000,000 years ago, and once inclosed all the hard parts have been as well preserved after that long interval, as they were immediately after being inclosed in the concretion. Lime concretions range from less than an inch in diameter to several feet through. They are not confined to shales, but sometimes occur in sandstones, in this case also usually having as a nucleus either a shell, or the bone, or bones, of some animal.

They are likely to be found anywhere in the limestone belt, from the Appalachian Mountains to the Rocky Mountains, or in the Great Basin, or on the Pacific Coast. Often they have been mistaken for turtles and other objects. A good many of the cases where the head or body of animals "petrified with all the flesh" are reported, it is one of these concretions which has a shape sufficiently like the part described, for the imagination to construct the rest.

Septeria
Pl. 69

Septeria are lime concretions, which, after they had formed, have shrunk and developed a series of cracks running through them in all sorts of directions, and since then the cracks have been filled with various minerals, such as calcite, dolomite, and siderite. These make a series of veins which intersect the concretion, in a sort of network. Septeria are mostly of considerable size, ranging from six inches in diameter to several feet through. They are characteristic of the shales of ancient sea bottoms, especially those of Devonian age in New York, and Pennsylvania, and those of Cretaceous age in Wyoming, Montana and the Dakotas.

Flint concretions The silica in limestones is often segregated into nodular masses of varying sizes, to make concretions of flint. Such masses have grown in the limestone, and, while growing, have either pushed away, or dissolved the adjacent limestone, so that the flint nodule is pure silica. They are especially characteristic of the chalk beds, and of ancient limestones which formed on the floor of the sea, like the Helderberg Limestone of New York, Pennsylvania, Ohio, etc. When thin sections are cut through these flints, and examined under the microscope, many remnants of the shells of plants and animals are still recognizable. A nucleus is seldom found, but in some cases there is a fossil in the nodule about which the concretion doubtless formed. The spicules of sponges, shells of diatoms, and of radiolarians seem to have contributed most of the material from which flint concretions are formed. In addition to the silica there are frequently inclosed in these nodules the horny jaws of various sea worms, and a host of spiny balls the relationships of which are still unknown.

Sandstone concretions There are two types of sandstone concretions, first those which are cemented with lime, and second those cemented with iron oxide. The concretions bound by lime are especially characteristic of sandstones which were laid down as river deposits, either in the channels or on the flood plains, and also the sandy deposits resulting from wind deposition. In these cases the concretions will mostly be found to have formed around some organic nucleus, most frequently about a bone, or group of bones, of some ancient animal. In this country they are mostly found in the arid and semiarid sections of the West, where the present day wind erosion exposes the harder parts of bluffs, etc.

The second type of sandstone concretion is the one in which the cement is most often limonite, less often hematite. These concretions are less dense than the lime ones, and in some cases the limonite is only precipitated at a distance from the nucleus, which has resulted in the formation of a hollow shell, filled with loose sand. This is especially characteristic of certain concretions, found in a gravel or coarse sand in the region of Middletown, Del.

Oolites   In large bodies of water like the sea and some larger lakes we find concretions which have formed, or are still forming, about tiny grains of sand, which are still being moved about by the waves and currents. In such cases not only are great masses of concretions formed but they have very clearly marked the concentric layering, which shows that they have increased in size, sometimes more rapidly and sometimes more slowly. Where great masses of such concretions have formed the resulting rock appears like a great mass of small eggs, whence the term oolite. The cement may be any one of several substances, but lime, silica, and hematite are perhaps the most common. Here and there are found larger or smaller masses

of this oolite. In some cases it would appear
that the material was precipitated by the action
of bacteria. Such for instance is probably the
origin of the Clinton iron ore, a bed of oolitic
hematite, extending from New York State all
down the Appalachian Mountains to Alabama.

Pisolite
Pl. 69

When the concretions, formed in
exactly the same manner as in the
case of oolite, are of a size bigger
than a pea, then the rock is known as pisolite.

OTHER CONCRETIONS

Though less abundant concretion may form
from still other substances. Hematite has been
mentioned, and when concretions are made of
this material, either they have been deposited by
bacteria, or were formed as limonite and the
water of crystallization of this latter mineral
driven off.

Manganese concretions are found on the floor
of the ocean at maximum depths, and brought to
the surface by dredging.

GEODES

Geodes are nodules, which, when broken open,
are found to be hollow and the cavity lined with
one or more minerals. They represent a special
case of minerals in a cave. There was in the
first place a cavity in the surrounding rock,
usually of sand or clay. As the water leached
through the surrounding rock, it became satu-

rated with one or more minerals and then coming into the cavity, deposited the minerals, either as crystals, or as a non-crystalline mass, lining the cavity. Thus the inside is often a beautiful cluster of bristling crystals, or it may be simply layer on layer of chalcedony of any color. Before this process had gone so far as to completely fill the cavity, erosion had dislodged the mass, and it has been found. One usually recognizes that it is a geode by the fact that it is far too light to be a solid rock, and then it may be carefully broken. They are characteristic of certain formations; so that having accidentally broken the first one, others can be carefully opened to display the beauty of the interior. The geode illustrated on Plate 70 is lined with quartz crystals, but near by were found many others, some of which had chalcedony and some jasper as a lining. Such crystal-lined nodules are usually called geodes so long as they occur in a softer matrix so that they are easily dislodged, and until they reach a size of three or four feet in diameter.

Pebbles

When picked up either from brook beds, sea beaches, or the open plain, there are few forms of rock which tell a story of the past more completely than do pebbles; and any one, who enjoys reading a story written in form, structure and composition, will find in pebbles one of the most satisfying and at the same time testing exercises. The story may be complex or simple according to what has happened to the parent rock, and to that is added what happened since the pebble left the ledge where it was a part of a great mass. One must not forget to take into consideration where the pebble was found and the character of its associates. This sort of exercise is recommended to all interested in rocks. It will yield something upon first trying, and more on prolonged study; and the fullness with which it is done will test one's knowledge of the meaning of rocks as nothing else will do. As a sample of this sort of exercise let us take the two pebbles illustrated on Plate 71.

The upper one is a common quartz pebble picked up in a New England brook bed. Such pebbles are common all over the country formerly covered by the glacial ice sheet. It is crystalline quartz, but the individual crystals are not distinguishable, and such quartz is typical as the filling of veins. It therefore goes back to a time when the rocks were fissured, probably in connection with the folding accompanying mountain making far to the north in Canada. Into the fissures thus formed seeped the water which had been leaching through the adjacent rocks, and it was saturated with silica which it had dissolved from those rocks. In the open fissure the quartz was deposited as crystals, which grew finally filling the fissure and crowding each other so that all the faces were obliterated. The quartz vein was complete, but it must have been far below the surface of the ground. Time must have passed, thousands of years of it, until, in the weathering away of the mountain system, the many feet of overlying rock were removed and this vein was brought to the surface. As the quartz is harder than the adjacent rocks, the vein soon projected as a ledge. The effect of changes of temperature in alternately expanding and contracting the rocks developed cracks, into which water worked its way, and then the breaking was hastened by the expansion which takes place when water freezes, and in exposed regions is so effective, because the freezing and thawing are so often repeated. Finally an angular fragment of quartz was dislodged and lay on the surface, resistant to the solvent power of the rain. In this case this happened just before the advance of the great ice sheet. When that came to the place where the fragment lay, it was picked up along with all other loose material and partly shoved in front of, but probably mostly carried frozen in the ice, and journeyed one, two, three hundred, perhaps a thousand miles. This took many years for the ice moved only a few feet a day. Finally however it came to the point where the ice melted as fast as it advanced, and our quartz fragment was dropped at the front of the ice sheet along with other great masses of till. Here there was abundant water, partly from the melting of the ice, and partly from the storms which must develop where there are such contrasts in temperature, as there would be over the ice, on one hand, and over the bare land in front of the ice on the other hand. A torrent picked up our fragment and started it on a second journey, banging against other stones as it rolled along down the stream bed, every time it struck another stone bruising the corners which soon became rounded. Thus from time to time during high water the quartz fragment, becoming rounder every time it moved, journeyed down stream, until it came to the point where the stream emptied into a lake. Here the current was checked and the stone dropped to the bottom along with other larger stones to make the delta at the mouth of the stream. There it lay as long as the lake existed, and would be lying now, but that in New England a tilting movement of the land tipped the north end of the lake up and the water all ran out. Then the stream began to flow over its own delta and in time of freshet tore a channel down through the old delta carrying the pebble still further down, until it came to the level stretch which represented the old lake's bottom and there it dropped the pebble in its bed. And there it was found and picked up to become the pebble which told the above story of its life, and to repeat it as often as anyone will look at it with a seeing eye.

The second pebble is quite a different one. It was picked up in a gravel bank along a railroad cut, just at the foot of Mt. Toby in Massachussetts, and the writer has used it many times to test his students, to see if they could read the story which it tells.

It consists of two sorts of rock, the one, angular fragments of a hornblende schist, the other, a fine-grained granite filling all the spaces between the fragments of schist, even in cracks less than a quarter of an inch wide. The schist is the older rock and in its first appearance represents a deposit of mud (clay and sand) on the floor of the ocean, well out from the shore, and somewhere off to the east of Mt. Toby, perhaps ten miles, perhaps more, from the place where it was found. This was back in early Palæozoic times, millions of years ago.

This deposit was buried by further layers of sediment on the sea bottom and cemented into a shale. Then during a mountain making period the region was folded, and the sediments were altered by the combined pressure and heat, our layer of rock becoming a hornblende schist. After that happened considerable time must have passed, but just how much is not indicated by the pebble, before another period of disturbance took place, during which this deep seated schist was faulted, and shattered to fragments along the line of breaking. This accounts for the angular fragments. Then into the fissure thus formed was pressed a molten magma, which while liquid enough to flow and be squeezed into every opening could not have been very hot; for not even the corners of the schist fragments are melted or altered, so as to appear any different from the mass of the schist. The molten magma cooled rather slowly, making a fine-grained granite. This must all have taken place far below the surface, or the magma would have cooled into a felsite or dense lava.

Again a long time must have elapsed, while the rock overlying our piece was eroded away, so it could come to the surface. Just about the time it did come to the surface, the Connecticut

Valley was formed by a great block, 95 miles long by fifteen to twenty miles wide, dropping down six or eight thousand feet (probably not all at once but by one or two hundred feet at a time) between two north and south faults. This took place in the Triassic Period. Of course the streams then began to wash sand and stones of all sizes into the hole. Our pebble was one of these While still an angular fragment, lying perhaps ten miles east of the Connecticut Valley, a stream started it moving, and as it rolled along the brook bed, it was battered and rounded to its present shape, and finally tumbled over a waterfall to the bottom of the great hole, which had been formed as described above. Here with other stones it formed part of a coarse gravel, coarsest near the sides of the hole, and finer toward the middle; for the material was further distributed in the bottom of the valley. Our stone stayed pretty near the side and was soon buried beneath hundreds of feet of similar material. The leaching water dissolved enough iron rust so that this acted on the lower layers as a cement and bound the whole mass into a conglomerate.

Here for some millions of years our pebble rested, while above it was piled sand and gravel and a couple of sheets of lava, until the hole was filled, and our pebble was near the bottom of the mass. Later movements of the land raised the whole region, fully six thousand feet, and erosion went on for other millions of years. The conglomerate and sandstone wore away faster than the metamorphosed rocks on either side of the filled valley, so that a new valley, the present Connecticut Valley, came into existence.

When our pebble finally came near to the surface on the side of Mt. Toby (a mound of conglomerate which somehow was protected and wore down a little less rapidly than the conglomerate on either side of it), it was just about the time of the glacial period. The great ice sheet went over the mountain removing all the loose material and some more of the solid conglomerate. This brought our pebble to the surface, but too late to be moved by the ice. However as soon as the ice left the Mt. Toby region, the rains fell, and in the further weathering of the conglomerate, the cement holding our pebble in place was dissolved and it was freed. At once a tiny brook started it rolling down the side of the mountain, a brook so small that when the pebble reached the foot of the slope it did not have power to carry it further. Here there gathered a fan-shaped mound of such pebbles, known as an alluvial fan. It rested here not over a couple of thousand years, when the Central Vermont R. R. cut a groove through the fan, using the material for ballast, and here the pebble was found and brought home.

METEORITES

Meteorites can hardly be called common, but there is always a chance of finding one, and their interest is so great, that none should escape because unrecognized.

Meteorites are visitors to the earth from space, and they bring to us knowledge of the composition of planets and solar systems, other than our own. It is of interest to note, that while they have brought to us some combinations of elements which do not occur in the earth, still they have not brought any element with which we were not already familiar. They are popularly known as "falling" or "shooting stars," though of course they are not stars, but only small masses of matter which are entirely invisible until they come inside our atmosphere.

In space there are many small (compared with the size of the earth) chunks of matter, each pursuing its solitary way around the sun, or wandering through space along paths entirely unrelated to the sun. From time to time one of these passes near enough to the earth, so as to be influenced by its attraction, and then comes rushing toward it at tremendous speed, 20 to 30 miles per second. As soon as it comes into the atmosphere, even the very attenuated atmosphere, a couple of hundred miles above the surface, friction heats the surface of the meteor until it glows, and by that light we see the so-called shooting star, often with a trail of luminous matter streaming out behind. Of course in using this term " shooting star," we understand the meteor is no star, for they are bodies as big as our sun, shining at distances billions of miles away.

As the meteor rushes through the atmosphere it may all burn up, no large fragment reaching the earth's surface. The luminous matter streaming out behind is material which has melted and dripped off the main mass. As this oxidizes and cools, that part which did not become gaseous will finally fall to the earth as fine dust. When however a meteor actually falls to the earth, its surface is still hot, though probably there has not been time enough for much heat to be transmitted to the interior. At any rate they do not show any alteration due to this cause. On landing and sometimes before they land meteors break into two or more pieces. When found the surface always shows the effects of the heat generated by the friction of passing through the air, the surface being smoothed, and covered with stream lines and melted out pits and hollows, and the outer surface consisting of a thin crust, making an appearance, which once seen, can hardly be mistaken.

There are two types of meteorites, those made wholly or largely of iron with some nickel, and appearing like great chunks of iron, and those which are stony and resemble a granite boulder. In collections the first sort, i.e. iron meteorites, are most abundantly represented, because most easily recognized when found. They consist of masses of iron and nickel with small amounts of other elements, ranging in size from the Cape York meteorite, which fell in northern Greenland in 1894 and was later brought by Peary to the American Museum, and weighs some 36 tons, down to small grains as small as a grain of wheat. The largest one which has fallen in the United States was the Willamette meteorite weighing some 15 tons, and falling 19 miles south of Portland, Oregon. These and all iron meteorites have the iron in crystalline form which is readily seen if the meteorite is cut, and the surface thus made polished, then etched with acid, which is put on and quickly washed off. Every meteorite has its particular pattern, as illustrated on Plate 72, and by these patterns can be identified. Meteorites have a high value and are eagerly sought by certain large institutions and collectors. Since the crystalline structure is so characteristic of each fall, when a new meteorite is found, it is usually cut in two, and one part retained by the finder or some institution; while the other part is cut into small pieces, an inch or two on a side and a quarter of an inch thick, but each large enough to show the characteristic pattern. These are distributed largely by sale to other collectors. Thus a great meteorite collection consists of a few large meteorites and a great many small portions of other meteorites.

The second type of meteorite is the stony meteorite. Where meteorites have been located as they fell and recovered, the majority of them were of this type, so that probably more than half of the meteorites which fall are of the stony type. However when the stony meteorite is exposed to weathering it takes only a very short time before the surface is eroded off and then such a meteorite looks like any other boulder and probably most of them fail to be recognized, and so have been lost. Because they have so much greater variety, they are in many ways of greater interest than the iron type.

It is desirable that every one have his eye out

for meteorites, and when found it is desirable that the fact should be reported to some one of the great institutions which collect them, such as the National Museum in Washington, or the American Museum in New York. Each one should be on record even if it is desired to keep it in a private collection.

FOSSILS

In the sedimentary rocks one is apt to find remains of some of the animals and plants that lived at the time the rock was forming. While the soft parts of animals decompose rapidly, shells and bones are likely to be buried in the sediments, and if the conditions have been favorable, these remains may be preserved more or less perfectly. All through the millions of years that sedimentary rocks have been forming in the sea, in lakes, on river flood plains and in wind swept deserts, there was an abundance of life, as much as there is today; and our knowledge of that life is derived from these buried fossil remains, so that fossils have a great historic interest.

However as there have lived and died several times as many different kinds of animals as live today, the study of fossils becomes a separate subject, which cannot be treated in this book. Should any collector of rocks and minerals come upon fossils, he is opening a new field, and it will be necessary to turn to other sources for their identification. General books on this subject are scarce, but one or two are given in the literature list.

MISCELLANEOUS ROCKS

A List of the Elements, the Abbreviations Used for Them, and Their Atomic Weight, Which Is Approximately the Number of Times Heavier They Are Than Hydrogen.

Name	Oxygen = 16	Name	Oxygen = 16
Aluminium, Al	27	Molybdenum, Mo	96
Antimony, Sb	122	Neodymium, Nd	144
Argon, Ar	40	Neon, Ne	20
Arsenic, As	75	Nickel, Ni	59
Barium, Ba	137	Nitrogen, N	14
Beryllium, Be	9	Osmium, Os	190
Bismuth, Bi	209	Oxygen, O	16
Boron, B	11	Palladium, Pd	107
Bromine, Br	80	Phosphorus, P	31
Cadmium, Cd	112	Platinum, Pt	195
Cæsium, Cs	132	Potassium, K	39
Calcium, Ca	40	Præseodymium	141
Carbon, C	12	Protoactinium, Pa	231
Cerium, Ce	140	Radium, Ra	226
Chlorine, Cl	35	Radon, Rn	222
Chromium, Cr	52	Rhenium, Re	186
Cobalt, Co	59	Rhodium, Rh	103
Columbium, Cb	93	Rubidium, Rb	85
Copper, Cu	64	Ruthenium, Ru	102
Dysprosium, Dy	162	Samarium, Sm	150
Erbium, Er	167	Scandium, Sc	45
Europium, Eu	152	Selenium, Se	79
Fluorine, F	19	Silicon, Si	28
Gadolinium, Gd	157	Silver, Ag	108
Gallium, Ga	70	Sodium, Na	23
Germanium, Ge	63	Strontium, Sr	88
Glucinum, Gl	9	Sulphur, S	32
Gold, Au	197	Tantalum, Ta	181
Hafnium, Hf	179	Tellurium, Te	128
Helium, He	4	Terbium, Tb	159
Holmium, Ho	165	Thallium, Tl	204
Hydrogen, H	1	Thorium, Th	232
Indium, In	115	Thulium, Tu	169
Iodine, I	127	Tin, Sn	119
Iridium, Ir	193	Titanium, Ti	48
Iron, Fe	56	Tungsten, W	184
Krypton, Kr	84	Uranium, U	238
Lanthanum, La	139	Vanadium, V	51
Lead, Pb	207	Xenon, Xe	131
Lithium, Li	7	Ytterbium, Yt	173
Lutecium, Lu	175	Yttrium, Y	89
Magnesium, Mg	24	Zinc, Zn	65
Manganese, Mn	55	Zirconium, Zr	91
Mercury, Hg	201		

TABLE OF GEOLOGIC TIME

Eras		Periods and Their Duration in Millions of Years	Important Physical Events	Important Organic Events
Cenozoic	Quaternary	Recent	Youthful land forms having high relief formed.	Dominance of man.
		Pleistocene Epoch 2 M.Y.	Period of glaciation; four great ice advances.	Heidelberg, Neanderthal, and Crô-Magnon man; extinction of large mammals.
	Tertiary	Pliocene Epoch 10 M.Y.	Continuing world-wide land elevation.	Intermigration of North and South American mammals. Transformation of ape to man.
		Miocene Epoch 18 M.Y.	Cordilleras, Alps, Himalayas formed. Widespread vulcanism-basalt flows in northwestern United States.	Culmination of modern types of mammals. Apes appear in Old World.
		Oligocene Epoch 10 M.Y.	Land dominant; seas marginal.	Carnivores and ungulates develop into importance.
		Eocene Epoch 20 M.Y.	Extensive sedimentation; seas marginal.	Dawn of the dominance of mammals. Reptiles subordinate.
		Cretaceous 65 M.Y.	Widespread epicontinental seas. Laramide revolution at close of period—Rocky Mountains formed.	Climax and culmination of reptiles, especially dinosaurs; first flowering plants and grasses.

Era	Period	Time	Physical Events	Biological Events
Mesozoic	Jurassic	38 M.Y.	Continent emergent; shallow seas on western North America.	Rise of birds and flying reptiles, first modern trees.
	Triassic	35 M.Y.	Continent emergent; seas marginal.	Rise of dinosaurs, cycads, and ammonites.
Paleozoic	Permian	35 M.Y.	World-wide continental uplift and mountain building. Widespread glaciation.	Extinction of most Paleozoic fauna and flora. First modern insects.
	Pennsylvanian	48 M.Y.	Continent alternately rising and sinking.	Great coal-forming forests, of ferns and seed-ferns.
	Mississippian	35 M.Y.	Low lands and widespread submergence.	Culmination of crinoids, numerous sharks.
	Devonian	40 M.Y.	Widespread submergence, local vulcanism.	First known land animals, first forests.
	Silurian	28 M.Y.	Widespread submergence, local deserts.	First lung fishes and scorpions, abundant corals.
	Ordovician	65 M.Y.	60% of North America below sea.	Climax of invertebrate dominance, first vertebrate.
	Cambrian	105 M.Y.	Widespread submergence.	First abundant invertebrate fauna, trilobites dominant.
Proter-ozoic		700 ± M.Y.	Long periods of granite intrusion, sedimentation, and mountain building.	Bacteria and seaweeds present. Most invertebrates probably present, but remains are lacking.
Arche-ozoic		800 ± M.Y.	World-wide intrusive igneous activity; some sediments.	Blue-green algae present, primitive one-celled plants and animals probably present.

BIBLIOGRAPHY

MINERALOGY

Getting Acquainted with Mineralogy. By G. L. English, 1936, McGraw-Hill Book Co. A beginning textbook of mineralogy.

Introduction to the Study of Minerals and Rocks. 3rd Edition, by A. F. Rogers, 1937, McGraw-Hill Book Co. Describes the commoner minerals systematically.

Dana's Textbook of Mineralogy. 4th Edition, revised by W. E. Ford, 1932, John Wiley and Sons. Detailed descriptions of minerals, their physical properties, and their occurrence.

Manual of Mineralogy. 15th Edition, by E. S. Dana, revised by C. S. Hurlburt, 1941, John Wiley and Sons. A textbook of mineralogy.

MINERAL ECONOMICS, GEOPOLITICS

World Minerals and World Peace. By C. K. Leith, J. W. Furness, and Cleona Lewis, 1943, The Brookings Institution. Physical, economic, and political trends in the mineral industry.

Minerals in World Affairs. By T. S. Lovering, 1943, Prentice-Hall.

Minerals Yearbook. U. S. Bureau of Mines. An annual volume presenting statistical data on the production of the mineral resources of the United States. Reports on individual minerals or rocks may be had separately.

ECONOMIC GEOLOGY

Mineral Deposits. 4th Edition, by W. Lindgren, 1933, McGraw-Hill Book Co. The manner of occurrence and origin of mineral deposits.

Elements of Engineering Geology. 2nd Edition, by H. Ries and T. L. Watson, 1947, John Wiley and Sons.

This Fascinating Oil Business. By M. W. Ball, 1940, Bobbs-Merrill Co. A simple and elementary description of the petroleum industry.

Geology of Coal. By O. Stutzer and A. C. Noe, 1940, University of Chicago Press.

GENERAL GEOLOGY

Down to Earth. By C. Croneis and W. C. Krumbein, 1936, University of Chicago Press. An introduction to geology, profusely illustrated.

BIBLIOGRAPHY

Textbook of Geology Part I—Physical Geology. 4th Edition, by C. R. Longwell, A. Knopf, and R. F. Flint, 1939, John Wiley and Sons. A standard text on geology.

Field Geology. 4th Edition, by F. H. Lahee, 1941, McGraw-Hill Book Co. Recognition and interpretation of geologic structures and topographic forms as they are observed, and methods of geologic work.

PRECIOUS STONES

A Book of Precious Stones. By J. Wodiska, 1910, G. P. Putnam's Sons. Written for jewelers, but of general interest.

The Curious Lore of Precious Stones. By G. F. Kunz, 1913, Lippincott. Legends and stories of the gem minerals.

The Magic of Jewels and Charms. By G. F. Kunz, 1915, Lippincott.

Popular Gemology. By R. M. Pearl, 1948, John Wiley and Sons. Scientific and industrial uses of gems, current information about their locality and production.

FOSSILS

An Introduction to the Study of Fossils. By H. W. Shimer, 1933, Macmillan Co. An introductory textbook about fossil plants and animals.

Invertebrate Paleontology. By W. H. Twenhofel and R. P. Shrock, 1935, McGraw-Hill Book Co.

Textbook of Geology Part II- Historical Geology. 4th Edition, by C. Schuchert and C. O. Dunbar, 1941, John Wiley and Sons. The story of the development of life through the ages.

INDEX

273

INDEX

Tourmaline crystals, growing amid feldspar crystals in a cavity in granite, from Paris. Me

Gold in quartz, from California

PLATE 6   281

Native silver in calcite

Argentite, the black masses throughout the white quartz

Pyrargyrite as it appears after moderate exposure
to the light.

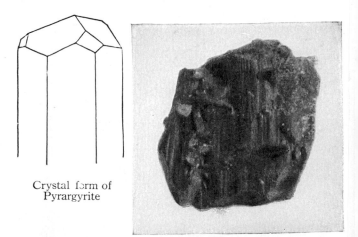

Crystal form of
Pyrargyrite

Prousite as it appears after moderate exposure to the light.

PLATE 8   283

Native copper from Michigan

Chalcopyrite in tetrahedrons and an occasional octahedron.

Chalcocite crystals with the bluish tarnish

Tetrahedrite crystals

PLATE II 285

Cuprite, the red crystals showing characteristic color, other showing the green tarnish of malachite

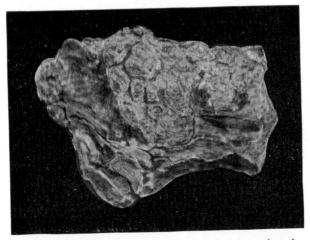

Malachite (green) and azurite (blue), the two minerals shown together as they very commonly occur

Limonite

The crystal form in which goethite is found, p is the prism faces, b and c are faces formed by beveling the edges of the prism, o is the pyramidal face characteristic of the ends

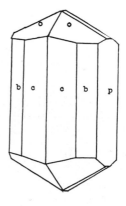

PLATE 13   287

Hematite, Clinton iron ore, oolitic

Siderite crystals

Pyrite crystals

Marcasite in concretionary form with radiate structure

PLATE 17   289

Galena in crystals

Pyromorphite crystals (green)

Sphalerite, some the normal yellow and some crystals with
the reddish tinge. (White is dolomite)

Zincite.

PLATE 21   291

Smithsonite in yellow crystals

Franklinite in octahedral crystals

Arsenopyrite, showing crystals massed so as to be incompletely developed

Realgar as it usually occurs in powdery incrustations

PLATE 25

293

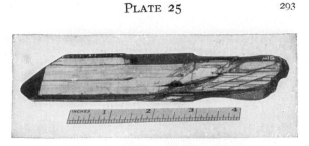

Large crystal of stibnite, the light colored face is the one
parallel to which cleavage occurs

Niccolite is a vein in slate

Cobaltite, silver color, with pink tinge

Smaltite, pink is cobalt bloom

PLATE 27   295

Carnotite from southwest Colorado

Cinnabar

Amethyst, not however deep enough colored for gems

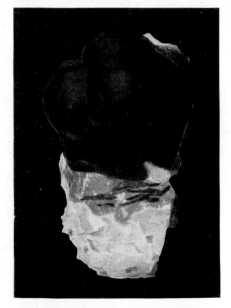

Jasper, with botryoidal surface

PLATE 32   297

Banded Agate from Brazil

Common Opal from Arizona

Siliceous sinter or Geyserite from The Yellowstone Park

PLATE 35

299

A group of Microcline crystals from Pike's Peak, Colo.

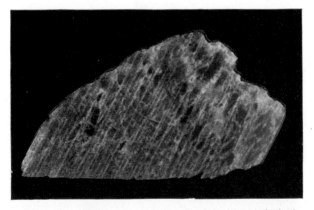

Labradorite, showing multiple twinning (the striation), and the iridescent play of colors

Crystal form of a pyroxene; *a* and *b* prism faces, *m* the beveled edge between two prism faces

Cross section of a pyroxene crystal showing the lines of intersection of the two cleavage planes

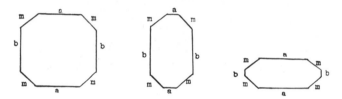

Cross sections of pyroxenes, showing typical forms taken by crystals

Augite crystals, in crystalline limestone

PLATE 38   301

The dodecahedron and the 24-sided figure characteristic of garnets

The garnet, grossularite

The garnet alamandite

Beryl of gem quality

Zircon in syenite

PLATE 40 303

Cyanite crystals in schist

A crystal of mica, showing basal cleavage

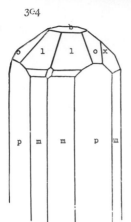

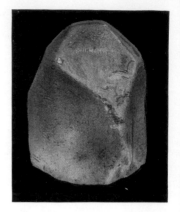

Crystal form typical of topaz

A topaz crystal from Brazil

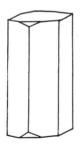

Crystal form typical of staurolite when simple

A typical twin of staurolite

PLATE 43 305

Serpentine

Chlorite

Apatite crystals in crystalline calcite

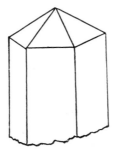
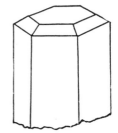

The ends of apatite crystals showing common modes of termination

PLATE 50   307

A group of fluorite crystals

A group of halite crystals

Amber

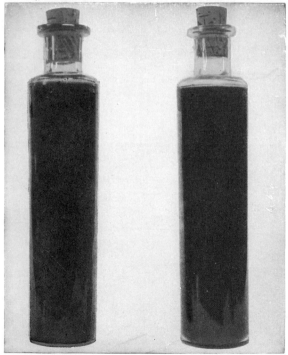

Two bottles of petroleum, the left hand one with a paraffin base, the right hand one with an asphalt base

PLATE 65   309

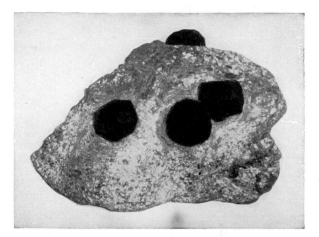

Mica schist, with garnets

Chlorite schist

Serpentine, composed of serpentine, hematite, and some
calcite

PLATE I   311

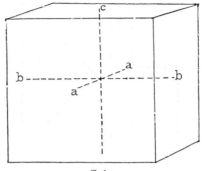

Cube

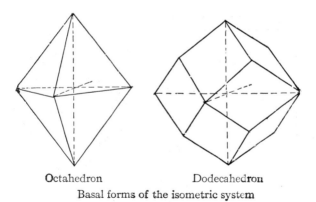

Octahedron   Dodecahedron
Basal forms of the isometric system

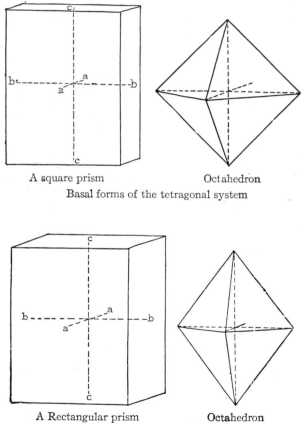

A square prism   Octahedron
Basal forms of the tetragonal system

A Rectangular prism   Octahedron
Basal forms of the orthorhombic system

PLATE 3   313

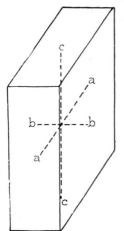

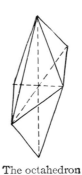

The rectangular prism askew   The octahedron

Basal forms of the monoclinic system

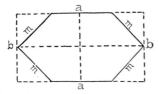

A cross section of the prism
with its edges beveled so that
the *b* faces are obliterated by the
m faces, and a six-sided prism
is formed (pseudo-hexagonal)

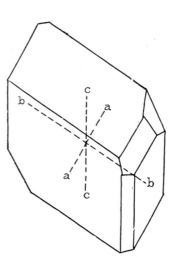

Basal form of the triclinic system

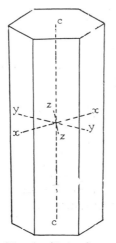

The six-sided prism

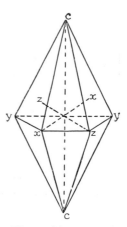

The double pyramid

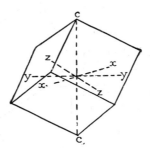

The rhombohedron

Basal forms of the hexagonal system

PLATE 10

315

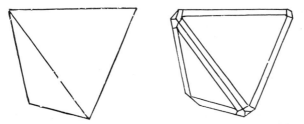

Tetrahedrons showing characteristic manner in which
tetrahedrite occurs

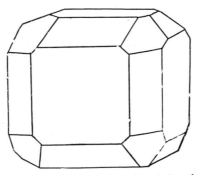

A cube with the edges beveled and
the corners cut in a form characteristic
of cuprite

Two intergrowing or twinned quartz crystals

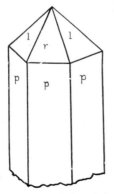

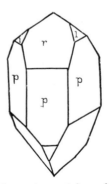

Diagram of the typical quartz crystal, *p* prism faces, *l* left hand rhombohedron, *r* right hand rhombohedron

A quartz crystal on which the left hand rhombohedron is represented by small faces while the right hand rhombohedron has large faces.

PLATE 14   317

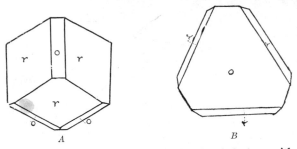

Crystal forms of hematite, *A* the rhombohedron with the edges beveled; *B* the tabular form, resulting from the excessive development of the two *o* faces opposite each other

A typical crystal of magnetite

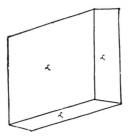

The rhombohedron typical of siderite

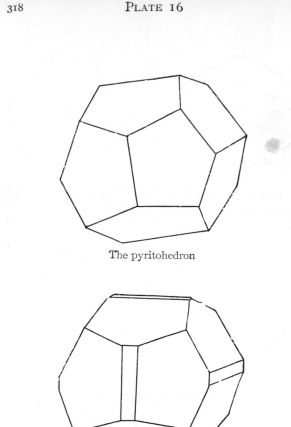

The pyritohedron

The pyritohedron with certain of its edges beveled by the cube faces, to show the relationship of these two forms

PLATE 18   319

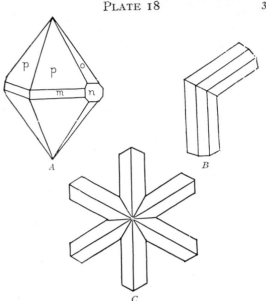

Typical forms for cerrusite; *A* the pyramid, *n* the
prism face, *m* the beveled prism, *p* the octahedral
face, and *o* the edge of the octahedral faces beveled;
B is the simple type of twinning; *C* is a multiple
twin where three crystals grow through each other

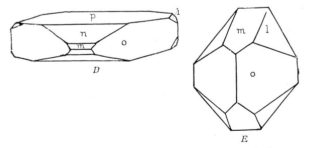

Forms in which anglesite occurs: *l* the pyramid face, *p*
the prism face, *o* the vertical edge of the prism beveled,
m the horizontal edge of the prism beveled, *n* a further
beveling of the horizontal edge of the prism. *D* the
tabular, *E* the prismatic form

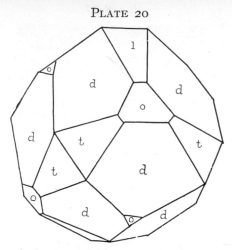

A characteristic form in which sphalerite
may occur; being the combination of, *d* the
dodecahedron, *o* the octahedron, and *t*, a
24-sided figure

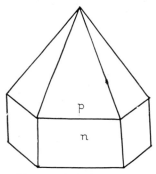

Characteristic form for zincite crystals, *n* the hexagonal
prism, and *p* pyramidal faces
on it

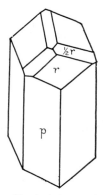

Typical form of
crystal of willemite;
p the prism, *r* rhom-
bohedron faces on
end, ½ *r* a second
lower rhombohe-
dron

PLATE 22

32I

Moss agates, showing the dendritic growth of manganitic minerals, like manganite or pyrolusite

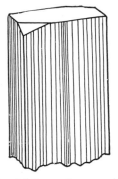

Crystal form of manganite

Crystals of green corundum in syenite, from Montana

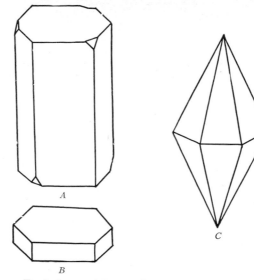

Typical crystal forms of corundum: *A* the elongated prism with the alternate corners cut by rhombohedral faces, *B* the tabular prism, *C* the double pyramid

PLATE 28   323

Cassiterite, twinned crystals

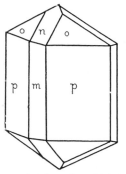

The crystal form in which both cassiterite and rutile occur when in simple crystals, *p* prism faces, *m* beveling of the prism, *o* octahedral face, *n* beveling of the edge between octahedral faces

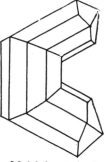

Multiple twinning characteristic of rutile

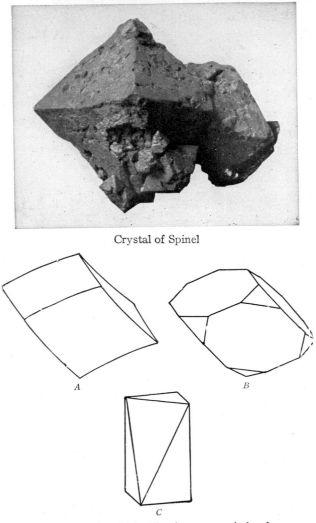

Crystal of Spinel

A

B

C

Crystal forms in which dolomite occurs; *A* the cleavage form, rhombohedron with the faces curved; *B* the rhombohedron with the corners cut, as it often occurs; *C* the form found in gypsum or anhydrite

PLATE 34

325

Orthoclase, a cleavage piece, *a* and *b* the perfect
cleavage planes, and *c* the imperfect cleavage plane

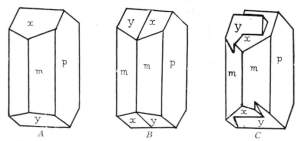

Crystal forms of orthoclase, *A* the simple crystal; *B* the
twinned form, and *C* the twinned form in which the crystals
are intergrowing

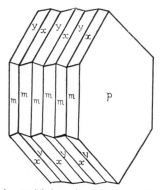

Diagram of a multiple twin of a plagioclase feldspar

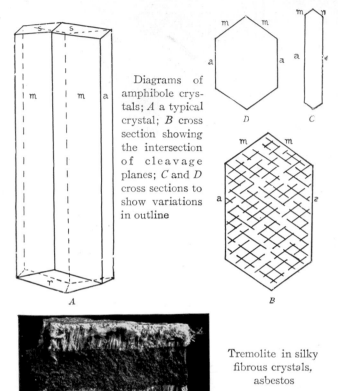

Diagrams of amphibole crystals; *A* a typical crystal; *B* cross section showing the intersection of cleavage planes; *C* and *D* cross sections to show variations in outline

Tremolite in silky fibrous crystals, asbestos

Hornblende crystals in quartzite

PLATE 42

327

Epidote crystals

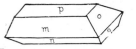

Typical forms of epidote crystals; *p* prism faces, *m*, *n*, *x*, and *y* beveled edges of the prism, *o* octahedral faces

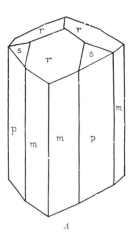

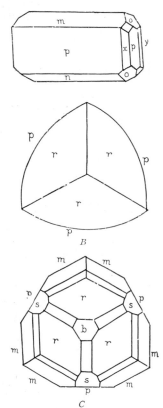

Typical forms of tourmaline; *A* side view; *B* and *C* ends to show terminations; *p* prism faces, *m* beveling of prism edges, *r* a low rhombohedron on the end, *s* the opposite rhombohedron, *b* basal face, and the other faces represent bevelings

A group of barite crystals

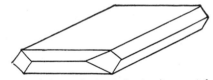

Outline of the typical tabular barite crystal

The six-sided double pyramid, composed of three interpenetrating crystals, typical of witherite and strontianite

PLATE 44 329

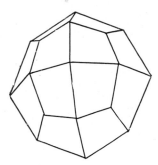

The typical form of analcite

A typical natrolite crystal

The typical crystal form of stilbite

A sheaf-like bundle of fibrous crystals, typical of stilbite

A group of calcite crystals

Typical forms of calcite; *A* the rhombohedron formed by cleavage; *B* a rhombohedral crystal truncated by the basal plane; *C* the scalenohedron; *D* the scalenohedron truncated by the rhombohedron: *E* the scalenohedron on a prism

PLATE 46

331

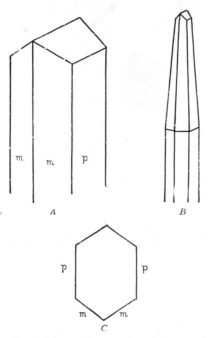

Typical forms of aragonite; *A* the simple
crystal; *B* a needle-like form, twinned; *C*
cross section to show how the form may
appear six-sided

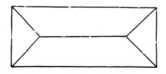

Typical form of the anhydrite crystal

A piece of gypsum looking on the surface of the perfect cleavage, and showing the two other cleavages as lines, intersecting at 66°. Twinning is also shown

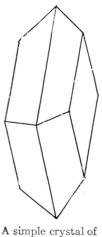

A simple crystal of gypsum

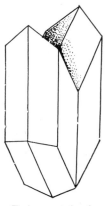

Twin crystals of gypsum

PLATE 51   333

Sulphur crystals

Ice crystals, the top one, the end of a hexagonal prism·
the two lower figures multiple twins as in snow flakes

PLATE 52

The Devil's Tower, Wyoming, and example of igneous rock with columnar structure, and resting on sedimentary rocks. Courtesy of the U. S. Geological Survey

PLATE 53   335

A coarse granite

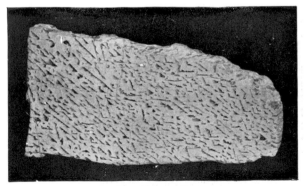

Graphic granite

Syenite

Gabbro

PLATE 55   337

Basalt-porphyry.   The large white crystals are phenocrysts of plagioclase feldspar

Basalt-obsidian

Amgydoloid

PLATE 57

The north face of Scott's Bluff, Neb., showing sedimentary sandstones above and clays below. The type of erosion is characteristic of arid regions. Courtesy of the U. S. Geological Survey

Breccia

Conglomerate

PLATE 59   341

Calcareous shale

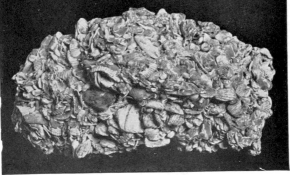

Coquina

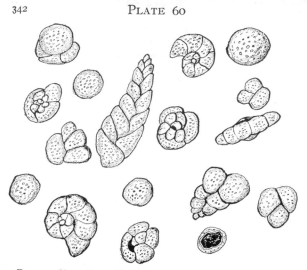

Foramenifera from Chalk; enlarged about 25 diameters

Encrinal Limestone; fragments of the stems, arms and
body of Crinoids

PLATE 62   343

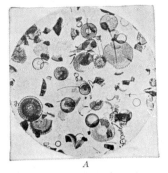

A

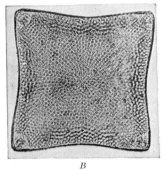

B

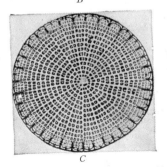

C

A diatomaceous earth magnified
50 times; *B* and *C* two diatoms from
the above enlarged 250 times. After
Gravelle, by the courtesy of Natural
History

A metamorphic rock, showing the contortion of layers due to expansion under heat

PLATE 64   345

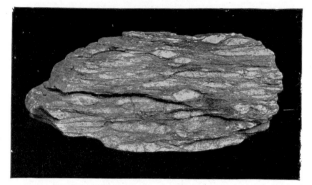

A conglomerate partly metamorphosed to a gneiss. Note the flattened pebbles and the alternation of the intermediate material to mica scales, etc.

A typical gneiss

Phyllite

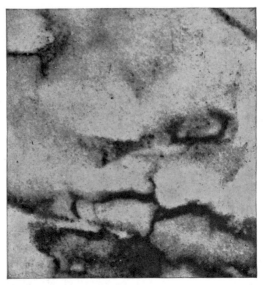

A white marble, with black streaks due to graphite

PLATE 68   347

Claystones, simple and compound

A line concretion, which on splitting disclosed a fern leaf
of the age of the coal measures

A septeria from Seneca Lake, N. Y.

Pisolite from Nevada

PLATE 70   349

A geode filled with quartz crystals

PLATE 71

A quartz pebble from the bed of a New England brook

A pebble of schist and granite from the foot of Mt. Toby, Mass.

PLATE 72   351

An iron-nickel meteorite, of 23 lbs. which fell in Claiborne
Co., Tenn.

An etched slice of an iron meteorite which fell in Reed
City, Osceola Co., Mich.

A stony meteorite, about natural size, which fell in 1875, in Iowa Co., Iowa